Never Give Up!

Never Give Up!

Eldonna L. Evertts / Language Arts
Lyman C. Hunt / Reading
Bernard J. Weiss / Linguistics and Curriculum

Edited by Jane Berkowitz and Craig Bettinger
Educational Consultants: Patsy Montague and Janet Sprout

THE HOLT BASIC READING SYSTEM
· LEVEL 11 ·

HOLT, RINEHART AND WINSTON, INC.
New York / Toronto / London / Sydney

Illustrated by

Tomi Ungerer, pages 16-34; Arthur Decker, pages 35, 99, 253; Joseph Cellini, pages 36-51; Bernice Myers, pages 52-56, 132-135, 222-225; Robert Shore, pages 58-70; Ingbet, pages 71, 183, 259; Betty Fraser, pages 72-81; Reynolds Ruffins, pages 82-98; Bill Morrison, pages 102-111; Philippe Fix, pages 112-129; Bob Goldstein, pages 118, 266; Irv Barnett, pages 131, 136; Tad Krumeich, pages 137, 220-221, 301, 313, 323; Tim and Greg Hildebrandt, pages 138-147, 282-291; Jerry Pinkney, pages 148-167; Douglas Gorsline, pages 168-182; Marie Michal, pages 186-193, 324; David Stone, pages 194-207; Lorraine Fox, pages 208-219; Ethel Gold, pages 226-241; Len Ebert, pages 242-252; Lawrence Di Fiori, pages 254-258; Ted Lewin, pages 260-269; Kyuzo Tsugami, pages 272-280; Jerry Zimmerman, page 281; Kenneth Longtemps, pages 292-300; Diane de Groat, pages 302-311; Miriam Schottland, pages 314-322. Photos, pages 212-213: Courtesy of the Mount Vernon Ladies' Association. Cover designed by Kay Wanous. Cover, pages 6-15, 100-101, 184-185, and 270-271 constructed by S. N. Studio.

Acknowledgments

Grateful acknowledgment is given to the following authors and publishers:

Abingdon Press, for "Pleased to Meet You," from *Scary Things* by Norah Smaridge. Copyright © 1969 by Abingdon Press. Used by permission.

Addison-Wesley Publishing Company, for "Homerhenry," adapted from *Homerhenry* by Cora Annett. Copyright © 1970 by Cora Annett. An Addisonian Press Book. Used by permission.

American Heritage Press and Jonathan Cape, Ltd., for "Alexander and the Magic Mouse," adapted from *Alexander and the Magic Mouse* by Martha Sanders and illustrated by Philippe Fix. Text copyright © 1969 by Martha Sanders. Illustrations copyright © 1969 by American Heritage Press. Used by permission.

Atlantic-Little, Brown and Company, for "Gertrude's Pocket," adapted from *Gertrude's Pocket* by Miska Miles. Copyright © 1970 by Miska Miles. Used by permission.

Brandt & Brandt, for "After the Party," from *Jonathan Blake* by William Wise. Copyright © 1956 by William Wise. Used by permission.

Coward, McCann & Geoghegan, Inc., and Russell & Volkening, Inc., for "George Washington's Breakfast," freely adapted from *George Washington's Breakfast* by Jean Fritz. Copyright © 1969 by Jean Fritz. Used by permission.

Thomas Y. Crowell Company, for "Company Clothes," from *In One Door and out the Other* by Aileen Fisher. Copyright © 1969 by Aileen Fisher. Used by permission.

Crown Publishers, Inc., for "The Pink Suit," adapted from *The Pink Suit* by Marilyn Hirsh. Copyright © 1970 by Marilyn Hirsh. Used by permission.

Follett Publishing Company and Brockhampton Press Limited, for "Gumdrop on the Move," adapted from *Gumdrop on the Move* by Val Biro. Copyright © 1969 by Val Biro. Used by permission.

Contents

Small Discoveries

Walking in the Fog (*poem*)   MARGARET HILLERT   15

Flat Stanley   JEFF BROWN   16
  Two Good Ideas   26

Never Make Fun (*poem*)   MARTIN GARDNER   35

Gertrude's Pocket   MISKA MILES   36
  Gertrude Spends Her Dollar   44

How to Keep Your Little Brother from Playing with the New Toy
You Just Finished Making All by Yourself...   BERNICE MYERS   52

AS PRETTY AS A PICTURE   57

Mexicali Soup   KATHRYN HITTE AND WILLIAM D. HAYES   58

Joe (poem)   DAVID McCORD   71

Elisabeth, the Bird Watcher   FELICE HOLMAN   72

Lazy Zuzka   ZLATA PACES   82
    The Three Spinners   88

WATCH THE SENTENCE GROW!   99

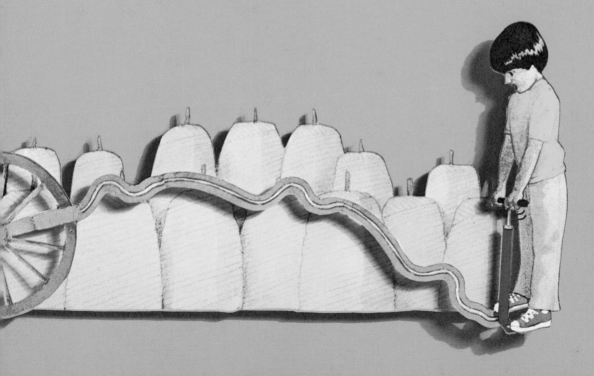

Animal World

Pleased to Meet You (*poem*)   NORAH SMARIDGE   101

The First and Last Annual Pet Parade   MARY NEVILLE   102
What Happened Next or The Last Part of the Story   108

Alexander and the Magic Mouse   MARTHA SANDERS   112
The Silver Medal   119

THE WINNER!   131

How to Find the Alligator You've Always Wanted and What to
Do with Him Then   BERNICE MYERS   132

The Spangled Pandemonium (*poem*)   PALMER BROWN   136

WITH OR WITHOUT?   137

A Walrus Named Boris   BERNICE MYERS   138

Homerhenry (*play*)   CORA ANNETT

    Act 1   148
    Act 2   152
    Act 3   155
    Act 4   158
    Act 5   161
    Act 6   166

Little House in the Big Woods   LAURA INGALLS WILDER   168
    Two Big Bears   171
    The Story of Pa and the Bear in the Way   177

Old Log House (*poem*)   JAMES S. TIPPETT   183

Never Give Up!

A Single Flower . . . *(haiku)*   HANNAH LYONS JOHNSON   185

The Case of the Silver Fruit Bowl   DONALD J. SOBOL   186

Mary of Valley Forge   DINA ANASTASIO   194
   Spring at Valley Forge   201

George Washington's Breakfast   JEAN FRITZ   208
   The Book in the Attic   215

LOOK IT UP!   220

Mummy Slept Late and Daddy Fixed Breakfast *(poem)*
   JOHN CIARDI   221

How to Keep the Cousin You Hate from Spending a Whole
Weekend at Your House and Maybe Even Longer...
    BERNICE MYERS   222

Where the Good Luck Was   OSMOND MOLARSKY   226
    The Leather Box   233

Fidelia   RUTH ADAMS   242
    A Beginning   250

WORD PICTURES   253

The Pink Suit   MARILYN HIRSH   254

Company Clothes (*poem*)   AILEEN FISHER   259

The Talking Leaves   BERNICE KOHN   260
    The Test   267

Other Places

Five Hundred Thousand Miles (*poem*)   MARCI RIDLON   271

Tikki Tikki Tembo   ARLENE MOSEL   272

The Optimist (*poem*)   281

Gumdrop on the Move   VAL BIRO   282
    Gumdrop Finds a Home   288

The Golden Treasure   MARYKE REESINK   292

FROM PORT TO PORT   301

The Round Sultan and the Straight Answer   BARBARA K. WALKER   302

The Forty Days   307

After the Party (*poem*)   WILLIAM WISE   313

When the Drum Sang   ANNE ROCKWELL   314

SAME SOUND — DIFFERENT WORDS   323

How Encyclopedia Brown Solved the Case of the Silver Fruit
Bowl . . .   324

GLOSSARY   325

Small Discoveries

Walking in the Fog

Out in the fog, out in the fog
All gray and misty white,
I hear some muffled scraps of sound,
But no one is in sight.

Only a voice, only a step.
I strain my eyes to see.
Then suddenly, suddenly from the fog
My friend steps out at me.

—Margaret Hillert

Flat Stanley

Story by Jeff Brown
Illustrated by Tomi Ungerer

"Breakfast is ready," said Mrs. Lambchop to Mr. Lambchop. "I'll get the boys up."

Just then their younger son, Arthur, yelled from the bedroom. "Come and look!"

Mr. and Mrs. Lambchop went into the boys' bedroom. "Look at Stanley's bed," said Arthur.

Across the bed lay a large bulletin board on which the boys pinned up pictures and things. It fell on Stanley in the night.

Stanley wasn't hurt. "What's going on here?" he called out from under the bulletin board.

Mr. Lambchop hurried to pick up the bulletin board. "Oh," he said. "Stanley's flat!"

"As a pancake," said Mrs. Lambchop. "Queerest thing I've ever seen. Let's have breakfast, and then Stanley and I will go see Doctor Dan."

"How do you feel, Stanley?" Doctor Dan asked. "Does it hurt very much?"

"I felt kind of funny for a while after I got up," Stanley said. "But I feel fine now."

"Well, that's how it is with these cases," said Doctor Dan. "We'll just have to keep an eye on this young man."

When Stanley got used to being flat, he liked it. He could go in and out of a room, even when the door was closed, just by going under the door.

Arthur tried to go under a door, but he hurt his head.

One day Stanley was walking with his mother when her ring fell off. It rolled down through the bars that covered a dark, deep hole in the sidewalk. Mrs. Lambchop began to cry.

"I have an idea," Stanley said. He took the laces out of his shoes and tied them together. Then he tied one end of the laces to his belt and gave the other end to his mother.

"Let me down slowly," he said, "and I'll look for your ring."

Mrs. Lambchop let Stanley down through the bars. He looked all over for the ring. At last he found it, and Mrs. Lambchop pulled him up.

"Thank you, Stanley," she said. "Having you flat is very handy."

One day Stanley got a letter from a friend who had moved to California. School was over, and Stanley's friend asked him to come to California for a visit.

"Oh, boy!" Stanley said. "I'd love to go!"

Mr. Lambchop said, "I can't afford to send you all the way to California by airplane. I'll have to think of some other way."

When Mr. Lambchop came home that night, he had a large brown-paper envelope. "Now then, Stanley," he said, "see if this will fit. Then we can afford to send you to California."

The envelope fit Stanley very well. There was even room left over for a sandwich.

The next day Mr. and Mrs. Lambchop slid Stanley into his envelope, along with the sandwich. They mailed him from the box on the corner.

Mrs. Lampchop was worried because Stanley had never been away from home alone before. She knocked on the box. "Can you hear me, dear?" she called. "Are you all right?"

"I'm fine," Stanley said in a loud voice.

Then Mr. and Mrs. Lambchop said good-by and went home.

Stanley had a fine time in California. When the visit was over, Stanley's friend returned him in a beautiful, large white envelope.

Back home Stanley told his family that he had had a wonderful trip.

On Sunday afternoons Mr. Lambchop always liked to take the boys off with him to a museum or to the park. But it was hard to hold on to two boys who were never still. It was easier after Stanley got flat. Mr. Lambchop rolled Stanley up and tied some string around him. Then he could carry Stanley by the string and hold on to Arthur with the other hand.

Stanley didn't mind being carried because he had never liked to walk. Arthur didn't like to walk but he had to, and it made him jealous of Stanley.

One Sunday afternoon the Lambchops met an old friend of Mr. Lambchop's. "Well, George, I see you have bought some wallpaper," the man said.

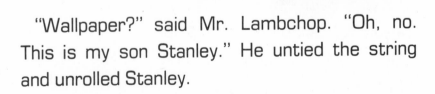

"Wallpaper?" said Mr. Lambchop. "Oh, no. This is my son Stanley." He untied the string and unrolled Stanley.

"How do you do?" Stanley said.

"Nice to meet you," the man said. Then he said to Mr. Lambchop,

"George, that boy is flat."

"Bright, too," said Mr. Lambchop. "Stanley does very well in school."

That night Mr. and Mrs. Lambchop heard a noise in the living room. They found Arthur on the floor with a great many large books on top of him.

"Put some more on me," Arthur said when he saw them. "Don't just stand there. Help me."

Mr. and Mrs. Lambchop sent him back to bed, and the next morning they had a talk with Stanley. "Arthur can't help being jealous of you because you're flat," they said. "Be nice to him. You're his big brother."

One day Stanley and Arthur were in the park. Many other boys were flying beautiful kites.

"Someday," Arthur said, "I'll have a big kite, and I'll win a kite-flying contest, and everyone will know me. **No one** knows me these days."

Stanley remembered what his mother and dad had said about Arthur's being jealous. He went to a boy with a broken kite and asked if he could use his string.

"You can fly me, Arthur," he said. "Come on." Stanley tied the string to himself and gave Arthur the string to hold. He ran across the grass. Then he turned to meet the breeze.

Up, up, up went Stanley, being a kite. He knew just how to fly on the wind. He went right into it if he wanted to go higher. And he let the wind take him from behind to go faster

Stanley was a beautiful sight, green and brown in the blue sky. Everyone in the park stood still to watch. No one ever flew the way Stanley Lambchop flew that day. Maybe no one ever will again.

After a while, of course, people grew tired of watching, and Arthur grew tired of running about.

Three boys asked Arthur to go with them for a hot dog. Arthur left the string stuck in a tree. He didn't notice that the string was getting all caught up in the tree. Stanley got stuck in the branches. Twenty minutes went by before Arthur heard him yelling and set him free.

Stanley would not talk to Arthur that night. He said he was sorry, but Stanley was mad.

Two Good Ideas

Mr. and Mrs. O. Jay Dart lived in the apartment above the Lambchops. Mr. Dart was in charge of the Museum of Art. At breakfast one morning, Stanley heard his father talking about Mr. Dart.

"I see," said Mr. Lambchop, reading the paper, "that still another great painting has been stolen from the museum. It says that Mr. O. Jay Dart is at his wits' end. The police and the guards can't seem to find the thieves."

Early the next morning Stanley heard Mr. Dart talking to his wife in the elevator. "These sneak thieves work at night," Mr. Dart said. "It's very hard for our guards to stay awake when they have been working all day."

That gave Stanley an idea. He told Mr. Dart all about it.

"Stanley," Mr. Dart said, "if your mother will let you, I will put you and your plan to work tonight!"

Mrs. Lambchop said Stanley could carry out his plan if he would rest all afternoon. "I won't have you up that late without some rest."

Early that night Stanley went with Mr. Dart to a big hall in the museum. Mr. Dart showed Stanley a very large painting. "That," he said, "is one of the greatest paintings in the world!"

Then Mr. Dart took Stanley to another room and said, "It's time for you to get ready." He took out a pretty white dress, some little shoes, a wide straw hat, a wig, and a stick.

"If you wear these," Mr. Dart said, "you'll look like a painting that belongs in the big hall."

Stanley was very upset when he saw the dress. "I'll look like a girl," he said. "I wish I had never had my idea." But he had promised to help, so he put on the dress.

Back in the big hall, Mr. Dart helped Stanley climb up into a picture frame across from the great painting. In the beautiful frame, Stanley looked just like a picture of a sheep girl.

Mr. Dart went off, and Stanley was alone in the big dark hall. Time went by and Stanley got tired. Anyone would get tired of standing in a picture frame. "Maybe the thieves won't come," Stanley thought.

The moon went behind a cloud, and then the big hall was really dark. Stanley heard a sound.

Creeeeeeeeek....

The strange sound came again. Then Stanley saw a light. A trap door had opened in the floor, and two men came up into the hall!

"This is it," said one of the thieves. "This is where we pull one of our biggest jobs while everyone sleeps."

"Right," said the other man. "In all this great city there is no one to see us."

The thieves took the great painting off the wall. Then one of the thieves looked over at Stanley.

"Look at the strange sheep girl in this painting," he said. "I thought sheep girls always smiled. This one looks scared."

Just in time, Stanley smiled.

"She looks happy to me," said the other man. "And what a pretty little thing she is, too."

Pretty! That really made Stanley mad. He waited until the sneak thieves had turned back to the other painting, and then he yelled in a loud, scary voice,

"POLICE! POLICE! MR. DART! THE SNEAK THIEVES ARE HERE!"

"I think I heard the sheep girl yelling," said one of the thieves quietly. "Oh, boy! Yelling pictures! We need a rest."

"You'll get a rest, all right!" yelled Mr. Dart, running in with the police and guards. Before they knew it, the thieves were led away to jail.

The next morning Stanley Lambchop had his picture in the newspaper.

For a while everywhere Stanley went people looked at him. He could hear them whisper, "Look at that boy over there. That's Stanley Lambchop. He's the one who caught the sneak thieves."

And then something strange began to happen. People didn't whisper anymore. They laughed and made fun of Stanley as he went by. They yelled mean things about the way he looked.

Stanley told his father how he felt. "It's the other children I mind most," he said. "They don't like me anymore because I'm different."

"It's not right to make fun of people because they're different," Mr. Lambchop said.

"I know," Stanley said. "Only maybe it's hard for everyone to like everyone."

That night Arthur heard Stanley crying. He went over to his bed. "Are you okay?" he asked.

"Go away," Stanley said.

"Please let's be friends." Arthur couldn't help crying a little, too. "Oh, Stanley," he said. "Please tell me what's the matter."

"The thing is," Stanley said, "I'm tired of being flat. I want to be like other people again."

Arthur could think of nothing to say. So he took hold of Stanley's hand. The two brothers sat together in the dark, being friends. They were still sad, but each one felt a little better

Then Arthur jumped up, turned on the light, and ran to a big box where toys were kept.

"Here it is," Arthur said. He had found what he wanted, an old pump. The boys looked at each other.

"Okay," Stanley said at last. "But take it easy." He put one end of the pump in his mouth.

"I'll go slowly," Arthur said. "If it hurts, wave your hand at me."

Arthur began to pump. At first nothing happened, but soon Stanley's face got a little round. Arthur watched Stanley's hand, but there was no wave, so he pumped on. Slowly Stanley began to get round.

**"It's working!
It's working!"**
yelled Arthur.

Stanley got bigger and bigger. The buttons on the top of his pajamas popped off. A minute more and Stanley was round again. Arthur stopped pumping. There stood Stanley as he used to be, as if he had never been flat at all!

"Thank you very much, Arthur," Stanley said.

The brothers were shaking hands when Mr. Lambchop came into the room with Mrs. Lambchop right behind him. "We heard you up and talking when you should be asleep!" said Mrs. Lambchop.

"George!" said Mrs. Lambchop. **"Stanley's round!"**

"I'm the one who did it," Arthur said.

Everyone was very happy, of course. And all the family told Arthur how wonderful he was.

Then Mr. and Mrs. Lambchop put the boys back into their beds and gave them each a good-night kiss.

Never Make Fun

Never make fun of a turtle, my son,
   For moving so slow in a race.
He *prefers* to move slow and he thinks that *you* go
   At a terrible, nerve-wracking pace.

Don't ever sneer at a beaver, my dear,
   Because of the size of his tooth.
He wonders why all of your teeth are so small,
   And thinks that *your* grin is uncouth.

It's vulgar to laugh at a baby giraffe.
   His neck is unusual, that's true.
But I tell you he's glad to resemble his dad,
  And would hate
    To be shaped
     Like you!

—*Martin Gardner*

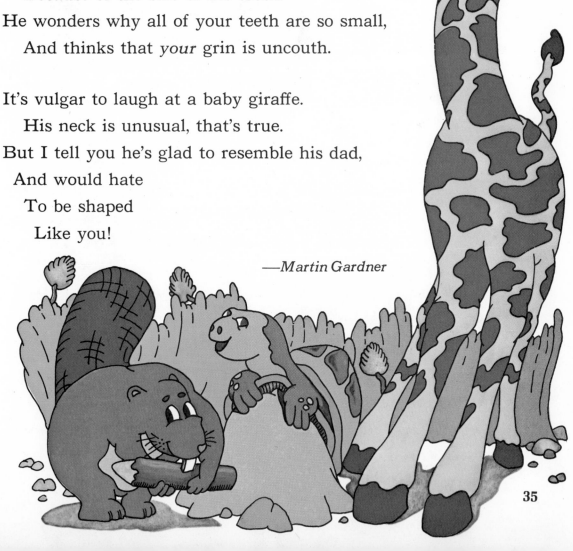

Gertrude's Pocket

Miska Miles

Gertrude walked home from school along the dirt path called "The Row." She thought how much she hated school and Watson Pike.

She looked at the houses along The Row. There was Watson's house, right in the middle. Watson, what a mean boy he was. And how she hated him. "Someday," thought Gertrude, "I'll fix that Watson Pike."

Just today Gertrude had found a big paper bag on her chair. Inside the bag something moved. Gertrude yelled and jumped as a fat snake pushed itself out of the bag and onto the floor.

"An old king snake never hurt anyone," Watson Pike said. Everyone laughed, even Gertrude's own brother, Jud.

"Watson," the teacher said, "take that snake outside."

Watson picked up the snake and waved it around in the air before he took it outside.

When Gertrude got home that afternoon, her mother was cooking, and her grandmother was making a dress.

"Time for school to be out already?" Grammaw asked. Grammaw always asked that because they didn't have a clock.

"Yes, Grammaw," said Gertrude.

"Was everything all right in school today?" Maw asked. Maw always asked that because she knew Gertrude hated school. "You're lucky to have a school so near home."

Maw moved a big pot away from the fire. "Everything is almost ready," she said. She went outside to get some air.

"There's a car coming," she said.

Gertrude ran out of the house and saw a big black car coming slowly up the road. From the doorway Grammaw said, "Look at that car coming along the road. Wonder where they think they're going?"

"They're lost, maybe," Maw said.

"Our road wasn't made for cars like that," Grammaw said.

Gertrude saw a man and a lady inside the car. "Can I get a little water for the car around here?" the man asked.

"I can get it!" Gertrude ran into the house for a pail and went down to the well.

The man hurried to meet Gertrude when she came with the water.

When he gave the pail back to Gertrude, he looked worried. "Will this road take us to the highway?" he asked.

"If you turn around," Gertrude said. "It's the other way."

The man climbed into the car and turned it around. Then he stopped. The lady put her hand out the window. "This is for you, little girl," she said.

The car moved on. In Gertrude's hand was a dollar bill. Gertrude could hardly believe her eyes. "It's a dollar," she said.

Grammaw took the dollar from Gertrude and went into the house. Gertrude went in after her. She saw Grammaw drop the dollar into a blue bowl.

"That was a nice little windfall," Grammaw said.

When Paw and Jud came in, they all sat down to eat. Grammaw and Gertrude told them what had happened.

"Wish I'd been home," Jud said. "What are you going to do with the dollar, Gertrude?"

Grammaw said, "I put it in the blue bowl."

Paw got up from the table and got the dollar. He looked at Maw. He didn't say a word, but she smiled. Then Paw looked at Grammaw.

"I know just what you're thinking," said Grammaw. "And you're right."

Paw said, "We all think you should have the dollar, Gertrude. It's yours."

"Gertrude doesn't have a pocket," Jud said. "Let me have it. It'll be her dollar. I'll just keep it safe."

"Give it to your sister," Paw said.

"What are you going to do with it?" Jud asked. "We need a ball. Everyone could play."

"She'll get what she wants," Paw said.

"Maybe she'll get a book," Jud said. "She's always reading. She even reads the newspapers on the wall."

Gertrude thought about what Jud had said. Maybe he was right. Maybe she should get something everyone could use. Maw would like it if she bought something for Grammaw, because Grammaw was always doing something for everyone. She even made Gertrude's underwear out of white sugar sacks. Grammaw would like a clock. The trouble was — Gertrude didn't want to get a clock for Grammaw. Not for a while anyway.

When everyone was through eating, Grammaw said to Gertrude, "Let's see if this fits."

It was a red dress, and it was made from one of Grammaw's old dresses. Gertrude tried it on.

"It's just beautiful," Gertrude said.

Gertrude went to school in her new red dress on Monday. Her friend Ellen was standing in the doorway waiting for her. Watson and three other boys were sitting on the school steps. As Gertrude walked by, Ellen yelled, "Watch out!" But it was too late. Watson had put his foot out and tripped Gertrude. Gertrude fell on the steps.

She looked down at her dress and saw a big rip in it. "You tore my dress." She wanted to cry, but she wouldn't let anyone see her cry — not anyone.

"I did not!" said Watson. *"You tore it on that nail."*

As Gertrude walked by The Row after school, she worried about the rip in her dress. She didn't want her grandmother to be too upset. When she reached home, Grammaw was taking clothes from the line, and Watson was there with Jud.

"Here comes Sugar," Watson called.

For a minute Gertrude didn't know what Watson was talking about. Why would he call her Sugar?

Then Gertrude noticed the clothes on the line. Watson had seen the word "Sugar" on her underwear. She walked up to Watson and looked him right in the eye. Watson looked right back at her. Gertrude took a deep breath. "Hello, Watson-One-Shirt," she said. Then she turned around and walked into the house.

"I heard you," said Grammaw. "That wasn't very nice to call him Watson-One-Shirt. He can't help it if he's got only one shirt."

"Well, he called me Sugar," Gertrude said.

"Now why would he call you that?" asked Grammaw.

"He saw the clothes on the line," said Gertrude.

Then Grammaw saw the rip in Gertrude's dress. "What happened to your dress?" she asked.

"I tore it on a nail at school," Gertrude said.

"Let me have a look," Grammaw said. "I'll put a pocket over the rip. It will be as good as ever."

Gertrude Spends Her Dollar

The next morning Gertrude put the dollar in her pocket. When she reached school, everyone was there.

"Here comes Sugar," Watson said.

"I don't care what he says," Gertrude told herself.

"And she's got a patch on her new dress," Watson said.

"This isn't a patch, Watson," Gertrude said. "This is a pocket."

Watson waved his arms in the air. "Look everyone! Sugar has a pocket and nothing to put in it."

"I've got a dollar bill!" Gertrude said and walked into the schoolhouse.

After school Gertrude waited until she was sure Watson had gone ahead of her. Ellen waited with her. They walked together along the road to The Row. They went by Watson's house, but he wasn't there. Then Ellen was home, and Gertrude hurried on alone.

At the end of The Row, Watson waited for her.

"Let me see the dollar," he said.

"No," said Gertrude.

"That dollar isn't real," Watson said.

"I'll show you." Gertrude took the dollar out of her pocket and said, "See? It's real."

Watson came up close to look. He grabbed the dollar and started running and laughing. Gertrude ran after him and grabbed him by the shirt. She heard Watson's shirt rip. It was a wonderful sound. She ripped it again and again. He wasn't laughing now. He threw the dollar at her. "There you are, Gertrude," he said.

Gertrude picked up the dollar, and put it in her pocket. She started home. Everything was wonderful. She stopped beside the stream and sat in the shade of a small tree. Tomorrow Watson wouldn't be in school. He wouldn't have a shirt to wear. And that was what she wanted. A jay flew by, and a thin squirrel sat up and looked at her.

After a while, Gertrude began to cry. She knew she had to tell someone what she had done. She went back to The Row and knocked on Watson's door.

Mrs. Pike opened the door.

"I tore Watson's shirt," Gertrude said.

"Well, his shirt was very old," Mrs. Pike said. "I'm sure it was easy to tear."

Gertrude took the dollar from her pocket. "I thought maybe you could get some cloth and make him another shirt."

"Well, Gertrude," said Mrs. Pike. "That's nice of you, but I know you didn't mean to tear it."

Gertrude could hardly get the words out. "I did mean to," she said. She put the dollar in Mrs. Pike's hand and ran home as fast as she could.

When Gertrude got home, she told her mother and grandmother what she had done. "I tore Watson's shirt," she said. "So I gave my dollar to Mrs. Pike to get some cloth for a new shirt."

"Well, maybe that's as good a way to spend it as any," said Gertrude's mother.

"Easy come, easy go," Grammaw said. "I can make the shirt when Mrs. Pike gets the cloth."

Watson wasn't in school the next day. When Gertrude got home that afternoon, Grammaw was making a bright blue shirt.

"Watson's shirt?" Gertrude asked.

"Watson's shirt," Grammaw said. "That dollar bought enough to make a shirt for Watson and a dress for you."

"Grammaw," said Gertrude. "I won't wear a dress that looks like Watson's shirt. I won't do it."

"Mrs. Pike thought she was doing something nice for you," Grammaw said.

"I don't care," said Gertrude. "I won't wear it."

"Do you want to hurt Mrs. Pike's feelings?" Maw asked. "Why don't you go off somewhere and think about it."

Gertrude went outside and sat on the steps. She sat there a long time. If she didn't wear the dress, Mrs. Pike would be hurt—and Grammaw, too. Gertrude knew there was nothing she could do about it.

She went inside. "I'll wear the dress," she said.

The shirt and the dress were ready by Saturday.

"I made Watson's shirt plenty big, so it will last him a long time. But I didn't have enough cloth to make the dress very long," Grammaw told Gertrude. "Try it on. It may be a bit short."

Gertrude tried on the dress.

"You won't be wearing that dress for very long," Maw said. "You're growing too fast."

That afternoon when Gertrude went outside, she saw Jud and Watson playing together near the road. Watson's new shirt looked nice. She looked the other way. She put her hand in her pocket. Nothing in it. Nothing for Watson to take. It would be all right — going to school on Monday.

And today — today she had everything she wanted. A few wild berries growing by the stream, a jay darting past, and a thin, old squirrel calling to her from the treetop.

Bernice Myers

How to Keep Your Little Brother from Playing with the New Toy You Just Finished Making All by Yourself...

Have you ever said to yourself,
"I'm going to make a toy or something."
And was your little brother listening?
Did he say, "Me too?"

Well here's how all that
can be different from now on.
Find all the things you need
to help you make the toy.
Carry them outside and
hide them where no one will find them.
If your little brother looks
at you a bit funny, make believe
you don't see him.

Whatever you do, don't make
the mistake of saying, "Get lost
you pest. Mind your own business."

52

He's sure to run right to your mother with those words— even adding some of his own on the way. It could put an end to any TV for the whole night.

He may come up close and ask, "What are you doing?" So think of an easy answer like, "Nothing."

If he doesn't believe you, say, *"I'm building a bunny bundle bowl with a crabtree charger plugged into a used tigerbutton sandwich."*

Even though *you* don't know what you're saying, he just might think *he* does. So while he's deep in thought, it's a good time to run outside.

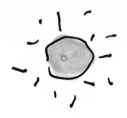

Have fun making your toy.
Of course, when you're finished,
your little brother
will quickly ask,
"Let me try it."

If you want to let him try it,
. . . then let him.

But if you feel real mean
that day, then here are a
few ideas you can try.

Just as he reaches out
to take it away from you, yell,
"Why don't you go and make your own?"

He might just think that's a good idea,
but more than likely he will
still want yours.

Begin to walk quickly
to your room as you say
out loud,
**"Oh, what an awful mistake.
It's horrible. I can't believe
it. How awful! Ugh!
I'm going to faint.**

"Ohooooooooo!"

Then lock your door.

Of course, if you have no room
or door, then start yelling . . .

**"Wait, don't touch it! See.
I knew it! This is *awful!*
You've made it very mad."**

Put your ear close to the toy.
*"What did you say? You don't like
my brother? Oh, no, he won't
hurt you. He won't even touch you.
I promise. You want HIM to promise?"*

Then turn to your brother
and make him promise
not to touch your toy.
In most cases that will
work.

The toy you made is all yours
until the day he finds out
it doesn't talk.
But maybe by then you will
be tired of playing with it
yourself and won't mind so
much if he uses it.
After all you're not really
a mean brother, are you?

As Pretty as a Picture

Sometimes we tell what something is like by comparing it to something else. Read each line below. Find the person it tells about.

as flat as a pancake
as busy as a bee
as mad as a hornet

Finish the sentences below in your own words.

Stanley was as flat as _____.
Grammaw was as busy as _____.
Gertrude was as mad as _____.

Mexicali Soup

Kathryn Hitte and William D. Hayes

All the way across town Mama sang to herself and her little one. There on the street of the great fine city, she sang a song from the old home in the mountains. And she thought of what she would get in the little stores.

Only the best of everything! Potatoes and peppers—the best! Tomatoes and beans—the best! The best garlic and corn! And then, cooked all together, ah! Mama's special Mexicali Soup. The soup that always made everyone say, "Mama makes the best soup in the world."

"Ah," Mama thought, "dinner tonight will be very special for my Rosa and Pablo and Juan and Manuel and Maria, and for my little one, and for Papa, too."

"Mama, Mama! Wait a minute," called Maria, running out of school with her new city friend. "May I play awhile with Ann? Please?"

"Very well," Mama said. "Awhile. But do not be late for dinner, Maria. I am making my special soup tonight."

"Mmm-mmm, Mexicali Soup!" Maria said. Then she looked thoughtful. "But, Mama?"

"Yes, Maria?" Mama said.

"Mama, there are such a lot of potatoes in your Mexicali Soup."

"Of course," Mama said, smiling.

"Ann doesn't eat potatoes. Her mother doesn't eat them. Her sister doesn't eat them. Potatoes make you fat, Mama," said Maria. "I think we should do what others do here. We are no longer in the mountains of the West, Mama, where everyone eats potatoes. We are in the city now. So would you—Mama, would you please

leave out the potatoes?"

"No potatoes," Mama said. She looked at Maria. Her face was thoughtful. "Well, there are plenty of good things in the Mexicali Soup without potatoes. I will put in more of everything else. It will still make good soup."

"Of course, it will," Maria said, hugging Mama. "You make the best soup in the world."

Mama went on with the little one to the street of the little stores, thinking as she went.
"Tomatoes,
beans,
corn,
green peppers,
red peppers, good and hot,
and garlic,
but *no potatoes!*"

Mama went to one little store for the best tomatoes and corn. She went to another for the best beans and garlic. "And the peppers," she said to the little one. "We will get the peppers from Pablo, our own Pablo, at the store where he works."

Pablo came hurrying out of the store to the little stand on the sidewalk.

"Let me help you, Mama! I hope you want something very good for our dinner tonight. I get very hungry working here," Pablo said.

"Yes, Pablo," Mama said. "For tonight—something special!" She reached for the hot red peppers. "Mexicali Soup!"

"That's great," Pablo said. Then he looked thoughtful. "But, Mama—"

"Yes?" Mama said, putting some peppers in a bag.

"Well—Mama, you use a lot of hot peppers in your soup," said Pablo.

"Of course," Mama said, smiling.

"A lot," Pablo said again. "People here don't do that. They don't cook or eat the way we did in the mountains of the West."

"I know, Mama. I have worked here for weeks now, after school and Saturdays. And in all that time, Mama, I have not sold as many hot peppers to other ladies as you use in a week. Please *don't put hot peppers in the soup,* Mama," Pablo said.

"No peppers," Mama said. She looked at Pablo. His face was thoughtful. "Well—there are plenty of good things in the soup without peppers. I will put in more of something else. It will still make good soup."

Pablo put the peppers back on the stand. "Of course, it will, Mama." He kissed her. "Everyone knows you make the best soup in the world."

Mama went on home with the little one. "Tomatoes, beans, garlic, corn," she said to herself. "Yes, I can still make a good soup with those."

She sang to herself as she walked across the street.

"Mama!" Juan and Manuel called. They left their game of stickball and ran over to Mama.

"Oh, boy! Groceries!" said Juan when he saw the bags. He opened one of them. "Tomatoes and corn—I know what we're having for dinner."

"Me, too," said Manuel. He looked into the other bag. "Beans and garlic. Mexicali Soup! Right, Mama?" Manuel smiled. Then he looked thoughtful. "But, Mama — listen."

"I am listening," Mama said.

"Well, I think we use an awful lot of beans," Manuel said. "They don't use so many beans in the school lunch. You know, Mama, they have different ways of doing things here, different from the ways of our town on the side of the mountain. I think we should try new ways. I think we shouldn't use so many beans. Mama, please make Mexicali Soup *without beans*."

"Manuel is right!" Juan said. "My teacher said only today that there is nothing that is so good that it cannot be made better, if we will only try. I think there may be better ways of making soup than our old way. Make the soup tonight *without tomatoes*, Mama!"

"No tomatoes?" Mama said. "And no beans? In Mexicali Soup?" Mama looked at the thoughtful face of Juan and at the thoughtful face of Manuel. Then she closed the bags of groceries carefully. She walked with the little one away from the play street.

"We will be hungry for your soup tonight, Mama!" Juan said.

Manuel called, "Mama! You make the best soup in the world!"

At home, Mama put the groceries on the table. She sang a little song that only she could hear. She stood looking at the food. No potatoes. No peppers. Tomatoes—Mama pushed the tomatoes aside. Beans—she pushed the beans aside. Mama sat down and looked at what was left. "Well," Mama said. "The soup will be a little thinner tonight."

The door opened and closed. Rosa came in. Rosa, the young lady of the family. "Hello, Mama. Oh, Mama—I hope I'm in time! I heard you were making—" She looked at the groceries on the table. "All the way home I heard it. The boys and Maria—they all told me—and Mama! I want to ask you—please! *No garlic.*"

"Listen, Mama. Last night, when my friend took me to dinner, I had such fine soup! The place was so beautiful, Mama. And no garlic at all in the soup!

"Just leave out the garlic," Rosa said, hugging Mama. "You make the best soup in the world."

A deep voice and many other voices called all at once.

"Mama! We are home, Mama!"

Then all of them, Juan and Manuel and Pablo, with Maria holding Papa by the hand —all of them came to stand in the doorway. Papa reached for the baby.

"I have heard of something special," Papa said. "I have heard we are having Mexicali Soup tonight."

Mama said nothing. But there was fire in Mama's eyes. She waited.

"Your soup, Mama . . ." Papa said. "It is the best soup in the world!"

"But you want me to leave out something? The corn, maybe? You want me to make my Mexicali Soup without the corn?" Mama asked.

"Corn?" Papa opened his hands wide. "What is corn? It is a little nothing! Put it in or leave it out," he said, hugging Mama. "It does not matter. The soup will be just as—"

"Enough!" Mama said. "Out of here—all of you!" Mama waved her arms wide in the air. There was fire in Mama's eyes again. "I have work to do. Go."

"But, Mama," said Rosa, "we always help you with—"

"*No!*" Mama said. *"Out!"*

Rosa and Juan and Manuel, Pablo and Maria, and Papa with the baby went away to the living room.

There was no sound coming from Mama. Then, the sound of a quiet song. Soon they heard the good sounds of the table being set for dinner.

Mama was singing a happy song from the old home in the mountains. Juan and Manuel, Pablo and Maria, and Rosa and Papa looked at one another and smiled. Mama was singing.

Then Mama's voice called to them. "The soup is ready. Come and eat now."

"Ah! That is what I like to hear," said Papa, jumping up with the baby. "The soup is ready before I have even started to smell it cooking."

"Mmm-mmm!" said Juan and Manuel, running for the big table.

"Mmm-mmm!" said Maria and Pablo and Rosa when they saw the hot soup on the table. "Our Mama makes the best soup in the world."

But what was the matter?

"This doesn't look like Mexicali Soup," said Maria, looking at the bowl before her.

"It doesn't smell like Mexicali Soup," said Pablo.

Juan put down his spoon.

Manuel put down his spoon.

"This is not Mexicali Soup," said Rosa. "This is nothing but hot water!"

Everyone looked at Mama. Mama smiled and sang the old song from the mountains.

"Did you forget to bring the soup, Mama?" asked Papa.

"No," Mama said, still smiling. "This is the soup. And it is just what you wanted. I made the soup the way my family asked me to make it.

"*I left out the potatoes that Maria does not want. I left out the peppers that Pablo does not want. I left out the beans that Manuel does not want. I left out the tomatoes that Juan does not want. For Rosa, I left out the garlic. And for Papa, I left out the corn, the little nothing that does not matter.*

"The **new** Mexicali Soup!
It is so quick! So easy
to make," Mama said. "You just
leave everything out of it."

Joe

We feed the birds in winter,
And outside in the snow
We have a tray of many seeds
For many birds of many breeds
And one gray squirrel named Joe.
    But Joe comes early,
    Joe comes late,
    And all the birds
    Must stand and wait.
And waiting there for Joe to go
Is pretty cold work in the snow.

—David McCord

71

Elisabeth, the Bird Watcher

Felice Holman

Elisabeth looked out the window and saw a chickadee standing in the snow.

"Papa," said Elisabeth. "He's looking for something to eat. Do you think we could build a bird feeder and take care of him for the winter?"

"Good idea!" Papa said.

After lunch, Elisabeth and her father began to build the bird feeder. When they were through, they hung the feeder on the sill of the picture window.

"We can watch the birds while they eat," said Elisabeth. "I'll put out some bread."

"Well," began her father. "Some birds like bread, but let's get some sunflower seeds. Chickadees and some of the other smaller birds like sunflower seeds best. We can get some corn for the larger birds."

Elisabeth and her father went to the feed store. When they got home, Elisabeth put the seeds and the corn in the feeder. Then she called, *"All right, birds, come and get it!"*

She went into the house and stood at the window and waited and waited. But not one bird came near the feeder.

"They must be shy," Elisabeth said.

"The birds might come if we stand where they can't see us," Papa said.

That turned out to be a good idea. In a few minutes the first chickadee flew down to the feeder. He picked up a seed and flew to a nearby tree, where he put down the seed. Then he made a hole in the shell with his bill. He took the seed out of the shell, ate it, dropped the shell on the ground, came back and snatched another seed.

"Oh, Papa, our bird feeder is working!" whispered Elisabeth.

"Here comes another bird," said Papa.

A big blue jay landed on the feeder. Unlike the chickadee, the blue jay just sat there eating and eating. He was very beautiful, but he ate too much.

"Save some seeds for the other birds," cried Elisabeth. The blue jay must have heard her, for he flew quickly to a tree.

In a minute a beautiful red cardinal came and sat in the bushes under the window. The cardinal looked at the feeder, but he didn't fly up to it. He flew to the ground. Then he ate seeds that the chickadee and the jay had knocked off the feeder.

"A cardinal would rather eat on the ground than from a feeder," Papa told Elisabeth.

After a few days, the birds weren't so shy. Elisabeth found she could stand very close to the window while they came to the feeder.

One morning while Elisabeth was still in bed, she heard a loud noise outside. She ran to the window and saw a big fat squirrel on the bird feeder. He was eating the sunflower seeds as fast as he could.

Elisabeth knocked on the window. The squirrel jumped off the feeder in surprise and ran away.

"What's all the noise?" Papa asked as he came into the living room.

"A squirrel was eating the bird food!" cried Elisabeth.

"We'll have to keep him out of the bird feeder," said Papa. "I'll cut the tops of the bushes so that he can't jump from them to the feeder."

Elisabeth put nuts on the ground for the squirrel while her father cut the tops of the bushes.

But the next morning Elisabeth and her father saw the squirrel on the feeder again. "What are we going to do?" Elisabeth asked her father.

"I've got an idea," said her father. "We won't put any seeds in the feeder at night. If the squirrel comes before we get up in the morning, he won't find anything to eat."

The next morning Elisabeth filled the feeder with seeds and corn. As she and her father stood and watched, the chickadees came to the feeder. Papa caught sight of the squirrel sitting in a nearby tree.

"You're too late, old boy," Papa said to the squirrel. "The birds got here first."

As he turned to go into the house, Elisabeth cried, "Papa! Look!" Papa turned around just in time to see the squirrel land on the feeder and start eating the seeds.

"That does it!" said Papa. "Come on, Elisabeth. We'll keep that squirrel out yet."

Papa and Elisabeth got some wire and put it across the tops of the bushes under the window.

"When the squirrel sees that wire, he won't come near the feeder," Papa said.

But the squirrel came the next morning. When Elisabeth saw him eating the seeds in the feeder, she ran to tell her father.

"*What!*" yelled her father. "How did he get through the wire?" He ran to the window and knocked on it. He saw the squirrel jump in surprise and squeeze through one of the holes in the wire.

"That squirrel really surprised me," said Papa. "I didn't think he could squeeze through those holes. Well, I'll fix *that!*"

Papa got some wire with smaller holes. "I'd like to see the squirrel squeeze through this wire," he said.

The next morning Elisabeth and her father got to the big window just in time to see the squirrel climb up the bushes and look at the wire.

They couldn't believe what they saw next. The squirrel hooked his paws into the little holes and started to walk upside down along the bottom of the wire. He walked like this until he reached the top of the wire. He climbed over it, ran to the bird feeder, and snatched the seeds.

"I give up!" said Elisabeth.

But Papa had one more idea. He got a small basket and put some fine wire around it. He made a long loop with the wire. Then he put a nail into the window frame to hold the wire loop. He hung the basket right in the middle of the big window. Elisabeth filled the basket with seeds.

When the squirrel came the next morning, he climbed to the window sill. He looked up at the basket and tried a few jumps to reach it, but it was too high. Then he tried to climb the glass, but his little paws couldn't hold on to it. He climbed up the window frame until he got as high as the basket. Holding on to the frame, he reached as far as he could across the glass with one of his paws. But the basket was just out of reach.

"Now we have him," said Elisabeth.

"But we'll do something for the squirrel," said Papa. "We'll take the old bird feeder that we made and . . ."

". . . fill it with food and put it on the ground for him," cried Elisabeth.

"Right," said Papa.

Elisabeth reached up and put some sunflower seeds into the basket. Then she called, "All right, birds, come and get it!"

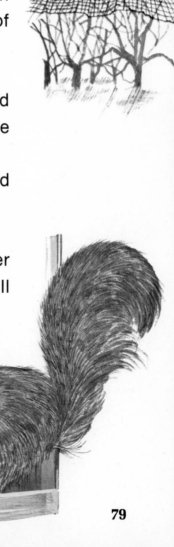

These are some of the birds that Elisabeth saw:

Chickadees . . .
they have little black
caps and black bibs.

Blue Jays . . .
they are bright blue.
They are beautiful,
but they make a lot
of noise.

Cardinals . . .
the father is bright red,
and the mother is
a lovely light brown.
They make a chipping sound
and have a lovely whistle.

Downy Woodpeckers . . .
they have funny short
tails, and the father has
a red spot on his head.

Nuthatches . . .

they have black caps,
great long bills,
and climb upside down.

Mourning Doves . . .

they look like small grayish-
brown pigeons and make a
sad *cooo, cooo, cooo* sound.
They eat on the ground,
and when they fly, their
wings make a whistling sound.

Goldfinches and Purple Finches . . .

they don't peck seeds open
like chickadees, but crunch
them right in their beaks,
and then leave the shells
on the feeder.

Lazy Zuzka

Zlata Paces

Once upon a time there lived a poor mother with a daughter named Zuzka. The mother and daughter were so poor they did not own anything, not even a cow. The only way they could make their living was by spinning flax.

Zuzka was a very beautiful and kind daughter. She had only one fault. She was lazy. Whenever her mother asked her to sit down at the spinning wheel, she started to cry. And when her mother made her spin, she sobbed even more. This angered her mother so much that one day she gave Zuzka a good beating. Zuzka cried so loud that she could be heard far away.

As luck would have it, the Queen was riding by at the same time. When she heard Zuzka's crying, she told her page to stop.

"Something horrible must have happened," the Queen said. "Let's see if we can be of help."

She went into the little house with her page. When she saw how sadly Zuzka was crying, she asked gently, "What is the matter, my lovely child?"

Zuzka's mother was so surprised to see the Queen in her poor home that she didn't know what to answer. She did not want to tell the Queen that she had a lazy daughter and that this was why she had had to beat her.

At last she answered, "Oh, good Queen, I have had great trouble with this child. She does not want to do anything else but spin flax. She would sit day and night by the spinning wheel. Today I asked her to leave her spinning to spend some time outside. I was afraid she would become sick from working so hard. But Zuzka would not stop spinning. It upset me so much that I beat her."

The Queen took a liking to the girl, and she liked the soft thread that is made by spinning flax. So she said to the mother, "If Zuzka really likes this work so much, give her to me and I will take care of her. At my castle I have the most beautiful flax in the world. If she works as hard there as she works at home, I promise you she will not be sorry."

Zuzka's mother was very happy to hear this, and she let her daughter go with the Queen to the castle.

When they got to the castle, the Queen took Zuzka by the hand and led her into three large rooms filled with beautiful soft golden flax.

Then the Queen said, "Work well, my girl. And when you have finished spinning all the flax you see in these three rooms, you will not be sorry. You will marry my son. And you will become a princess."

The Queen called for a golden spinning wheel.
Then she left Zuzka alone in the first room. Her
heart sank when she saw the flax.

Poor Zuzka sat down by the window and
started to cry. She sobbed so sadly that even a
stone would have been moved. She saw that she
could not finish all the spinning in a lifetime.
And she was so lazy she knew she could
not finish even part of it.

Zuzka sat through the night with these thoughts.
And she cried through the morning without
doing any work at all.

At noon the Queen came to see how much soft
flax Zuzka had spun. How surprised she was to
see that Zuzka had not touched one bit of flax.

"Zuzka," the Queen said. "Why haven't you
spun the flax?"

"My Queen," Zuzka cried. "I have never been
away from home before. I am so homesick and
lonely that I cannot work."

The Queen felt sorry for Zuzka. "Don't be sad, my child," she said. "But work well tomorrow so that you may marry the Prince."

After the Queen had gone, Zuzka again sat down at the window, looked outside, and did not work.

At noon the next day, the Queen came to see Zuzka again. When she saw that Zuzka had not touched the flax, her face turned red with anger.

This time Zuzka said, "Please understand, dear Queen. You see, I have sobbed so hard that my head hurts, and I cannot spin the flax."

Once again the Queen believed Zuzka. But on her way out, she said, "This is the last time I will ask you to start working. If you really want to marry my son and become a princess, you must spin the flax at once." And the Queen left poor Zuzka alone again.

But even on the next day, Zuzka did not touch the flax. Just as on the two days before, she did not even look at the spinning wheel. She only sat at the window and looked at the beautiful garden.

At noon the Queen came to the door. And when she saw that Zuzka had not touched the flax, she became even more upset than before.

"Listen to me, Zuzka. Today is the last day. If you have not spun the flax by tomorrow, you will not marry my son. You will be put in a dark cave full of snakes, frogs, and worms. And you will not have any food. You will not be lazy anymore."

With these words, the Queen turned and walked out of the room.

The Three Spinners

Zuzka could not stand to think of what would happen if she didn't finish the flax by the next day. Her hands started to shake when she thought of being put into a dark cave filled with snakes, frogs, and worms.

At last she started to spin. But she cried so hard that she couldn't do much. She cried and cried all day.

Then, just at sundown, she heard a knock at the window. She lighted a lamp, looked out, and saw three ugly old women. The first one had a very large lip. It was so fat that you could hardly see her chin. The second one had a large thumb on her right hand. It was so large that it covered the inside of her hand. The third one had a large right foot. It was so big that it looked as flat as a pancake.

When Zuzka saw the three ugly women, she jumped away from the window. But the old women smiled so kindly at her that she was not afraid. She opened the window and let them into the room.

"Oh, you beautiful child. Why are you crying?" the women asked.

Zuzka answered bravely, "Oh, how can I help but cry when I have to spin all the flax in this room and in two other rooms?"

And Zuzka told them everything that had happened to her. She even told them that the Queen had promised her that she could marry the Prince.

"But how can all this happen?" Zuzka asked. "In a lifetime I could not spin all this flax."

The ugly old women started to laugh. One of them said, "If you promise to ask us to your wedding and to let us sit at your table without being ashamed of us, we promise to spin all the flax for you. You will be surprised at how fast we can do it."

"Oh, I won't be ashamed of you. I will do anything you ask. Just start spinning at once," Zuzka cried.

The next morning Zuzka saw beautiful glittering thread all over the room. Her heart was filled with joy. There was only a little flax in the first room.

"What beautiful thread," Zuzka cried. "And how fast you work. You will soon be finished with this room full of flax."

"It is easy for us," the women said. "But we must go now. Tonight we will return."

At noon the Queen came to see Zuzka. She did not think that she would see any work done. How surprised she was to see the glittering thread.

"Zuzka," she said. "This is the most beautiful thread I have ever seen. How happy I am that you have worked so well and have not been lazy."

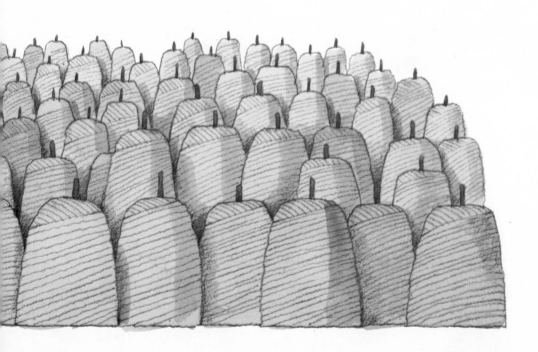

When night came, the three spinners were
standing at the window. Zuzka opened it quickly
and let them in. No longer was she afraid of
them.

And so it was, every night at sundown the
three spinners came, and at sunup they left. And
while Zuzka was asleep, they kept spinning the
flax into thread.

Every day at noon, when the Queen visited
Zuzka, she could not say enough good things
about the beautiful glittering thread and
Zuzka's hard work.

"My dear child," the Queen said. "How sorry I
am that I told you I would put you in a dark
cave. You are not a lazy girl, and you will marry
my son, the Prince."

The three spinners were now working in the second room, and the flax was disappearing. When it was all gone, the Queen began to get ready for the wedding.

At last the three spinners had finished spinning the flax in the third room. There was no more flax to spin.

Zuzka thanked the good women with all her heart. "You have saved me from the dark cave and helped me to become a princess," she said. "I will never forget you."

"Just don't forget your promise, and you won't be sorry," they answered. And as the old women went out the window for the last time, the sun was just coming up.

At last it was Zuzka's wedding day. The Prince was so pleased with the beautiful young girl who was to be his wife that he said to her, "Ask anything from me, and it will be done."

When the Prince told her this, Zuzka remembered the three ugly old women and so she answered, "I have at home three old aunts. They are poor but very kind and brave, and they have been very good to me. Please let me ask them to my wedding."

"Of course you may," said the happy Prince.

On the wedding day, just as people were sitting down to the wedding dinner, the doors opened and there stood the three ugly old women. When the young wife saw them, she went over to them and said, "Come in, my aunts. Please come and sit down with me." Then she brought them to her table.

People looked at each other. They would have laughed, but nobody wanted to anger the Prince. The Queen and the Prince were ashamed because of the funny-looking ladies. But the Prince could not go back on the promise he had made to Zuzka.

Zuzka took care of the women. She saw to it that they had all the food they wanted, and nobody laughed at them.

When the dinner was over and everyone got up from the table, the Prince came over to the woman with the large lip. He asked, "Dear woman, please tell me how do you happen to have such a big lip?"

"From spinning, kind Prince,
from spinning,"
answered the woman.

The Prince turned to the second woman with the large thumb and asked, "Dear woman, why do you have such a big thumb?"

"From spinning, dear Prince,
from spinning,"
she said.

At last he went to the woman with the foot as flat as a pancake and asked her why her foot was so flat.

"From spinning, dear Prince,
from spinning,"
she said.

When the Prince heard this, he became afraid. He thought of his beautiful wife and of all the spinning she had done. He hurried to her and said, "Zuzka, I have promised you that you will have anything you want. But there is one thing I will not let you do. You must never so much as touch a spinning wheel again."

At once the three women disappeared from the castle, and nobody knows where they went. But Zuzka thanked them in her heart every time she thought of them.

Zuzka did what the Prince wished. Never again did she touch a spinning wheel!

Watch the Sentence Grow!

You can start with a short sentence and add more and more information to make the sentence grow and change.

Boys play.
Boys and girls play and sing.
Good boys and happy girls play violins
and sing songs.

You can make the sentence even longer by adding words that tell where, when, how, why. Add some of these words to the sentence and see how it changes.

at school	in the morning
on the stage	after school
all over town	at six o'clock
loudly	because it's fun
softly	so people can dance
proudly	because they like music

Animal World

Pleased to Meet You

A tiger with a hungry smile,
A large and scaly crocodile,
A grizzly bear with big, sharp claws,
A lion with enormous jaws
Would not be very nice to meet
If you were strolling down the street.

But when you see them in the zoo
Just smile, and ask them "How d' you do?"
Since they're locked IN and you're
           locked OUT
There's nothing to be scared about.

—*Norah Smaridge*

The First and Last Annual Pet Parade

Mary Neville

In our town there had never been anything like a pet parade before. Some people said that the first annual pet parade got started the summer that firecrackers got ended.

Others said it wasn't the firecrackers. The parade got started because Mrs. Van Horn was looking for something to manage. There is plenty to manage in an annual pet parade.

George and I were afraid to put our big dog in the parade because she hated cats. But we should have known that Mrs. Van Horn would have thought of that. Dogs would be together in one part of the parade. Between the dog part and the cat part would be goats, fish, and turtles. It is hard to fight a turtle.

The biggest pets would lead the parade. These would be horses and ponies. Littlest pets would follow. Wonder what they'd be. A bee? A butterfly?

Prizes were going to be given to the biggest, the littlest, the oldest, the youngest, and lots of others.

The parade would gather at the school, move across the bridge, over the river, and end at the library. Prizes would be given there.

An awful lot of dogs and cats were cleaned up around town that week. So were a few pigs — small ones.

The day came! George said, "Hurry up. Do you think they're going to hold up the parade till you get there?"

"No," I said.

Down on Washington Street it looked awfully full of people and animals. My brother George and I were in the dog part. We never did see the first part of the pet parade. But we could hear it. There were people yelling and animals tramping around up there. There were horses, I think, some ponies, a few burros, and a homesick sheep.

We were all waiting around in the middle of Washington Street, holding on to our animals. Our dog got to know the most dogs she ever had known at one time before.

At last we began to move. Slowly the pet parade moved on a little at a time. All the people along the street waved and called.

George and I never did see the back end of the pet parade. And it kept getting farther and farther back.

Some little girls had their pets in doll buggies. It was hard for the little girls pushing doll buggies with pets in them to keep up.

George's friend, Herbie, was getting tired of pulling his wagon with the cage of mice in it. Our part of the parade was all the way between Cherry and Maple Streets, but getting closer to the bridge.

"I hope the bridge will hold the parade," I told George.

"Don't worry," said George. "The new bridge could hold a parade of elephants."

But George and I forgot something. The same thing about the bridge floor Mrs. Van Horn forgot!

Now the luckiest people in the pet parade were the pony riders who got to carry messages from the first part of the parade to the back. Just then one of these pony riders came tearing along and calling,

"Wait! Stop! Something awful is happening up ahead."

"Now what?" said George.

"It's the bridge!" someone called.

The thing we all forgot was the floor of the bridge. It had spaces in between for the snow to go through in winter. We found out that the animals with little feet would not go out on that bridge. Their feet would go right through the spaces in the bridge. They stopped. They wouldn't follow the big animals across the bridge. But the back end of the parade didn't get the message in time. And the parade started to pile

up

on

itself.

The dogs began snapping at each other. Cats were climbing up the trees. The big animals were going across the bridge and then coming back again with the others. And the scared little pigs jumped out of their doll buggies.

Mrs. Van Horn hurried by, and we heard her cry,

"We have lost control of our pet parade."

It was true.

What Happened Next
or
The Last Part of the Story

How the parade was ever going to get moving again, I didn't see. Soon all the animals would be after each other. Their owners would give up, and everyone would just go home. No prizes! No *nothing!*

I felt like crying. It was such a mess.

George said, "Try to keep smiling. A pet parade should be happy."

The police car had made it around the parade. The police were standing in the street, trying to get things moving.

Suddenly, around the corner into this mess came the ice cream man's truck. Because of the noise, no one heard his bell. And around the other corner came Mr. J. P. Cutler in his big, black car. George and I knew what was going to happen one second before it did. They met!

Mr. J. P. Cutler climbed out and saw that there was not much of a dent in his big, black car. The ice cream man looked sadly at the mess of ice cream all over the place. Ice cream on the sidewalk! Ice cream on the street! Ice cream on the bridge!

"Great!" George said. "Hurry before it's melted."

"Here, hold my mice," Herbie said to George. "I'm going to get some ice cream for free!"

"Hold your own mice," George told him. Then George looked at me. "It's your turn to hold the dog."

And he was off.

Then suddenly Mr. J. P. Cutler surprised everyone. "It is my pleasure—" he called out, "my great pleasure to ask each and every one of you to have some ice cream."

He waved some green money in the air. It made the ice cream man smile.

And each and every one of us had ice cream.

Then the meat-eating animals were eating melted ice cream. And the plant-eaters were eating melted ice cream.

How the parade got moving again was wonderful! Another police car came along. Mrs. Van Horn got out with all the blue, red, and gold prize ribbons.

Then Mrs. Van Horn ate some ice cream while Mr. J. P. Cutler held up his hand and said, "It will be my pleasure to give out prize ribbons as soon as we restore order."

George was back by me. So he gave me a push and said, "Why don't you be quiet and restore order?"

So I did. And everyone else began to restore order, too. Then the prize ribbons were given out.

People did say, however, that the firecrackers *might* have been more quiet.

Martha Sanders

Alexander
and the
Magic
Mouse

There was once an Old Lady who lived in a house on top of a hill. At the foot of the hill was a river, and on the other side of the river was a town.

The Old Lady was never lonely, for she lived with her animal friends:

a Brindle Cat,

a Magic Mouse,

and an alligator

named Alexander.

When the Brindle Cat wasn't sitting in the sun, he was thinking about how to catch the Magic Mouse. But the Magic Mouse had made herself invisible. The Cat couldn't catch her.

Each day the Old Lady put out food for the Magic Mouse, and each day the Brindle Cat got ready to catch her. The Magic Mouse had been invisible for so long, though, that the Brindle Cat had really forgotten what to look for. So he always fell asleep.

On hot days Alexander would go down the hill to the river and swim near a sign the Old Lady had put up. It said,

That was to keep people away. Alexander wasn't dangerous at all though. He was really very gentle. But the Old Lady knew people would be scared of him. Alexander felt that if he smiled enough, people would know that he was gentle and not at all a dangerous animal.

Sometimes when he was swimming, he would stick his head out of the water to see if anyone was near. But the few people he saw always cried, *"Help!"* and ran away. That made Alexander very sad.

The animals all loved the Old Lady. When the Old Lady was young, she went to many far-away lands. She always came home with something different. That's how the Brindle Cat and Alexander the gentle alligator came to live with the Old Lady and the Magic Mouse.

The Magic Mouse came with the house. She had always been there.

Each afternoon at five o'clock, the animals came into the living room to have tea and cakes with the Old Lady. They told her what had happened that day.

The Brindle Cat had to promise not to try to catch the Magic Mouse while they were all having tea. Even though the Magic Mouse made herself invisible, she was never too sure of the Brindle Cat.

The Old Lady would put a bit of cake on the table near the yarn basket, and soon it would be gone.

Sometimes, as the cake disappeared the Brindle Cat would forget himself and reach for the Magic Mouse. The Old Lady would look at him and say, "Now, now," and he would put his paws down again.

One fine afternoon in May, as they had all just sat down to tea, a little voice came from the yarn basket. Everyone was very surprised because the Magic Mouse was shy and didn't say much.

The Magic Mouse said,

"It is going to rain for
thirty days and thirty nights!
My tail tells me so,
and my tail is always right.
We must get ready!"

The Old Lady got up and went to the window. There wasn't a cloud in the sky. "Are you sure?" she asked.

"My tail tells me so, and my tail is always right,"

said the Magic Mouse, and that was all she would say. Her feelings were hurt, so she wouldn't say when the storm would begin.

"Let us think," said the Old Lady, sitting down again. "We must have plenty of logs for the fire, plenty of candles, plenty of food, and plenty of books to read."

While Alexander got the logs and the Old Lady made sure there was enough food and candles, the Brindle Cat finished his cake and went to sleep.

The next morning it began to rain. By lunchtime the drops were coming down hard and fast. Alexander made a fire and the Old Lady read stories out loud. From time to time they looked out the window at the rain. *What a wonderful storm!*

But in the middle of the night the Old Lady jumped out of bed to light a candle and went downstairs to the living room. "Magic Mouse, Magic Mouse!" she whispered.

"*Yes?*" answered the Magic Mouse in a sleepy
voice.

"Do you think the people in the town know
it's going to rain for thirty days and thirty
nights? Surely the river will flood the town,"
said the Old Lady.

"*No one knows but us,*" said the Magic Mouse.

"We must tell the people in the town about
the flood," the Old Lady said at breakfast the
next day.

She put on her dress and went quickly out the door. But soon she was back. "It's too muddy out there."

"You could write a letter," said the Brindle Cat, "and I'll go."

"Yes, yes, a letter to the Mayor," said the Old Lady. She wrote:

Dear Mr. Mayor:
    I am sorry to tell you that it is going to rain for thirty days and thirty nights and the river will surely flood your town. You must think how to stop it.
                Your neighbor,
    The Old Lady on Top of the Hill

The Brindle Cat took the letter and went out into the rain. But soon he was back. "The water has covered the bridge and I can't get across the river," he said.

"Then I'll go," said Alexander, "for I can swim any river."

"Be very careful, Alexander," said the Old Lady. She put the letter in his mouth, and off he went.

The Silver Medal

Alexander slid down the muddy hill, right into the river. He began to swim, holding his head up high so the letter wouldn't get wet.

He swam as hard as he could, but the river was very strong. As he swam, Alexander didn't think he was strong enough to get across the river. He was frightened and trembling. But he kept on swimming, and soon he reached the other side.

But where was the town? He had been carried right by it! Now he had to walk back. It was a long way, and Alexander wasn't used to walking, even a little way. He walked along slowly, tired from his hard swim. At last he saw the town.

A man with an umbrella was hurrying down the street through the rain. Alexander went up to him, smiled, and asked where the Mayor lived. But the man dropped his umbrella and ran down the street trembling and yelling,

"HELP!

HELP!"

120

The man made Alexander very sad. Then he saw a lady. He smiled at her, but she dropped her umbrella and ran inside a store. Other people ran away when they saw Alexander. The alligator was left all alone. He sat down on the sidewalk, and tears rolled down his face.

Soon a little boy came along. Alexander smiled at him through his tears. The little boy stopped.

He said, "Hello! What's the matter?"

"Hello," said Alexander. "I've got to find someone who will give this letter to the Mayor. Do you know where he lives?"

"Yes," said the boy. "He lives at the end of the street."

"Would you give him this letter?" Alexander asked.

"Sure," said the boy, as he reached into Alexander's mouth.

"Oh, thank you so much," said Alexander. "Don't forget."

"I won't. Good-by!" cried the boy.

Meanwhile, in the house on top of the hill, the Old Lady walked up and down, up and down. Night had come, and still Alexander had not come home. "Where can he be?" she asked. The animals were quiet.

"I'm hungry," said the Brindle Cat. "Let's have dinner."

After dinner the Cat went to sleep. The Old Lady kept going to the door and looking out into the rainy night. At last it was time for bed. But the Old Lady could not sleep. She got up in the middle of the night and went downstairs to the living room.

"Magic Mouse, Magic Mouse!" the Old lady whispered. "Is Alexander safe?"

"I think so," said the Magic Mouse in a sleepy little voice.

It was still raining the next morning. The Old Lady went up to the roof of her house and looked through her telescope. At first she could see nothing but rain. Then she thought she saw people building something—a wall made of bags of sand! So the Mayor did get her letter!

But where in the world was Alexander? She looked through the telescope all morning, but there was no sign of Alexander. The Brindle Cat had to go up to the roof to tell her it was lunchtime.

In the afternoon the Old Lady looked through her telescope and saw an awful thing. The sandbag wall was higher, but the river was higher, too. Which would win, the wall or the river?

By five o'clock it was too dark to see anymore. The Old Lady was just about to call everyone to tea when she heard a sound at the door. She ran to the door and there was Alexander!

He was muddy and cold and tired and hungry. As soon as he got inside, he began sneezing and trembling. *"Quickly! A cloth and some hot tea!"* cried the Old Lady. They dried him off, gave him some tea and some dinner, and put him to bed. But Alexander kept on sneezing. No one would say so, but everyone was very worried. Alexander was sick.

The next morning the Old Lady went to look through her telescope. She saw a big wave coming down the river. The flood! It came closer and closer. But the townspeople had made the wall very high. The Old Lady took a deep breath. The wave came to the wall and almost went right over the top—but it didn't! The wall was strong enough to hold back the water. The town would be safe! The Old Lady went to tell Alexander the news.

Alexander was still sneezing. The Old Lady felt his head. It was very hot. "Oh dear!" she said.

"Oh, dear, oh dear," said the Brindle Cat, who had come to see how Alexander was. But the Magic Mouse could not be found.

That night the Old Lady sat beside Alexander's bed. At last she got up and went downstairs. "Magic Mouse, Magic Mouse," she whispered. "How can I help Alexander?"

"Look on the tea table," said the Magic Mouse in a sleepy voice.

There lay a little white cake with pink writing on it. It said,

"Oh, thank you, Magic Mouse!" whispered the Old Lady. She went up to Alexander's room and put the cake inside his mouth. As he swallowed it, he smiled, thinking it was teatime.

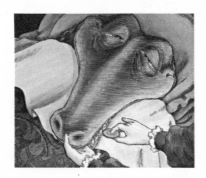

The next morning it was as rainy as ever, but Alexander felt much better. After breakfast he and the Brindle Cat played a game. The Old Lady was watching the river and the wall through her telescope. The town looked safe.

Every day it rained and rained and rained. The Old Lady was running out of food. The Brindle Cat was tired of playing games. Even the Magic Mouse was tired of sitting around and ate a hole in the yarn basket.

One day the Old Lady got out of bed with a funny feeling. Something was different. It was very quiet outside. Then she knew. The rain had stopped.

It wasn't long before the river got smaller. The townspeople took away the sandbags and began building a new bridge. Soon the great rain and the flood were almost forgotten.

One summer afternoon the Old Lady and the animals heard some lovely music. When they opened the door, they saw the Mayor and the townspeople.

The Mayor began his speech. "Dear Lady, you were not forgotten," he said. "The townspeople and I want to thank you for what you did. I wish to give you this silver medal."

"Oh, no, it's not for me, it's for Alexander!" said the Old Lady. As she gave the medal to Alexander, she told the Mayor about the night that Alexander swam the river.

The Mayor and the townspeople stayed for tea. Everyone told Alexander how brave he was. After they all had left, the Old Lady looked at Alexander. "It's a lovely medal!" she said to him.

"What's so great about a medal?" the Brindle Cat said. He was jealous, of course.

Alexander looked at his medal in the mirror and smiled. Tears of joy ran down his face. And inside the yarn basket the Magic Mouse smiled, too.

THE WINNER!

These animals were all winners in a pet show. Can you tell what each one got a blue ribbon for? Read the sign below.

PET SHOW   Prizes given to the
biggest softest
smallest slowest

All the underlined words end with *est*. When we compare more than two things we often add *est* to words. What animal might win a prize for being *fastest? smartest? strongest?*

Bernice Myers

How to Find the Alligator You've Always Wanted and What to Do with Him Then

If the one thing
in the whole world you've
always wanted is an alligator,
then here is how to get one . . .
without even leaving home.

You can send away for it.

As soon as the box comes,
open it carefully.
When you throw
away the stuffing from
the box, make sure you don't
throw away the little bird inside.
He acts as the alligator's toothpick
and always sits on his back.

Now that you have the alligator,
what will you do with him?

132

While he is small,
he will make a nice pet.
Children you never saw before
will want to play with you.
It's a great find for
show-and-tell, or for your
exciting science project.

After you have him for
a while, you will notice
that he is getting bigger
and bigger.

133

Soon he will be so big
that you will no longer
be able to take him for a walk,
have him sleep in the bathtub,
or hide him
from Grandma.

Don't be too sad.
He can still be a lot of laughs
around the house.
Stand him up in the corner
near the door on rainy nights.
Put him on the floor near the
fireplace.
Show him to friends who
come to visit and then
stay too late.
They will leave almost at once—
sometimes forgetting to take
their hats and coats
and other things
with them.

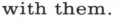

An alligator makes a good
hiding place.

Try hiding there when you
drop cake
or paint on the rug.
No one will ever think
of looking for you
in an alligator.

Just make sure he's already
had his breakfast.

The Spangled Pandemonium

The Spangled Pandemonium
Is missing from the zoo.
He bent the bars the barest bit,
And slithered glibly through.

He crawled across the moated wall,
He climbed the mango tree,
And when his keeper scrambled up,
He nipped him in the knee.

To all of you, a warning
Not to wander after dark,
Or if you must, make very sure
You stay out of the park.

For the Spangled Pandemonium
Is missing from the zoo,
And since he nipped his keeper,
He would just as soon nip you!

—Palmer Brown

With or Without?

The suffixes *ful* and *less* are added to words to change their meanings. The suffix *ful* means *full of.* The suffix *less* means *without.*

The boy felt <u>hopeful.</u>
The boy felt <u>hopeless.</u>

Which of the underlined words means *without hope?*

Which of the underlined words means *full of hope?*

Match these four words to the pictures below.

careful   thoughtless
careless   thoughtful

A Walrus Named Boris

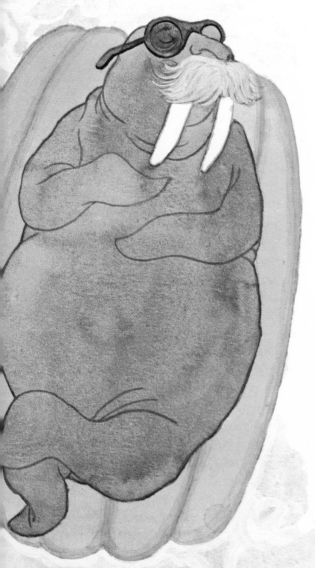

Bernice Myers

A walrus named Boris
Lived in a zoo,
And much of the time
He had nothing to do.

He would swim in the water
And sit in the sun
And jump for a fish
Just to please everyone.

Thought Boris, "How sad
To sit here all day.
I'd take Herman's place
Anytime...right away!

"I'd like to be Herman
and take care of the zoo.
I'd work all day long.
And have plenty to do."

"I'd feed all the animals,
Clean out the cages
And quiet the tigers
That went into rages."

As Boris was thinking
Of what he would do,
If he were the one who
Took care of the zoo,

Herman was walking
Past Boris's cage
And said, "I am working
Too hard for my age.

"How good it would be
To sit there all day
Like you, my dear Boris,
And just sleep and play."

139

Then Herman told Boris
He'd thought of a way
That each could be happy
The very next day.

And early next morning
The whole zoo could see
It was Boris, not Herman,
Outside with the key.

And inside the cage
On a rock in the sun,
Old Herman, the zoo man,
Just sat having fun.

The walrus was happy
And Herman was, too,
But the animals weren't,
"We'll move from the zoo!"

Boris tried to work fast
But then supper was late
And cleaning the cages
Would just have to wait.

The monkeys were starving
They leaped up and down,
The camels were angry
And ran all around.

The flies and the fleas
Moved in by the dozens,
They liked it so much
They called all their cousins.

"It's not all the fun
I thought it would be,"
Said Boris. "This zoo is
Just too much for me."

Boris got rid of
The flies and the fleas.
At last he could rest
And he dropped to his knees.

When Boris had done
All his work for the day,
He wanted to sleep.
But where could he stay?

So he said to himself,
"If I just use my head,
I think I could sleep
In Herman's big bed."

He knew Herman's house
Was not far away.
Thought Boris, "How long
Will his wife let me stay?"

"If I say very little
And try not to fight,
She'll think that I'm Herman
We look quite alike."

He climbed up the stairs
And opened the door.
"Dad!" children shouted.
There were dozens, or more.

"Sit down here, my love,"
Herman's wife said to Boris,
"And see what a supper
I've just cooked up for us."

He sat down to supper
And still no one knew
That in place of their daddy
Sat a walrus in blue.

143

He was sitting quite still
When he saw on a dish
A most happy sight —
A big beautiful fish!

Now Boris was starving
He'd been waiting all day
For the smell of that fish
That came floating his way.

With one great big jump
He leaped out of his chair
And ate that big fish
In one bite...in mid-air.

That gave him away,
And the wife shouted, "Oh!
This isn't my Herman
Let's all make him go."

Then poor frightened Boris
Leaped right to the floor,
Ran out of the house
And slammed the big door.

But soon right behind him
Came the children and wife,
And Boris the walrus
Had to run for his life.

Poor Boris thought, "Oh,
To be back in my cage.
This is clearly no life
For a walrus my age."

But Boris ran on
Till he came to the zoo.
He ran to his cage.
"I've had it! I'm through!"

145

"Herman, open this door,"
Shouted Boris. "Be quick!
Your wife and your children
Are making me sick!"

Boris got back in his cage,
Slammed the door,
And in no time at all,
Fell asleep on the floor.

But when Herman's wife
Looked in Boris's cage
And saw poor old Herman,
She went into a rage.

And when Herman looked out
And saw his dear wife
He was never so frightened
In all of his life.

He could see she was angry
And ready to fight
So he said that he'd stay
At the zoo for the night.

Then Boris and Herman
Fell asleep in the cage.
And the next day the wife
Was all over her rage.

That's how Boris found out
That his life at the zoo
Was better by far
With nothing to do.

Now he swims in the water
And sits in the sun
And jumps for a fish
Just to please everyone.

HOMERHENRY

A Play by Cora Annett

The Players

MR. HOMER, a tailor
MR. HENRY, a shoemaker
HOMERHENRY, a horse
POLICEMAN
FARMER
DIRECTOR OF HORSE SHOW
CIRCUS MANAGER
FIRST CLOWN
SECOND CLOWN
THIRD CLOWN
PEOPLE AT THE CIRCUS

Act 1

Time: Morning.
Place: A shoemaker's shop on a big street in the middle of town.

MR. HOMER. I have something to tell you. It's something I've never told anyone before.

MR. HENRY (*looking up from the shoe he is working on*). Yes?

MR. HOMER. I would like to be a horse.

MR. HENRY. Yes, I understand. I have wanted to make a pig of myself from time to time.

MR. HOMER. No, no. I want to be a real horse. And I know exactly how to do it. But I can't do it unless you help me.

MR. HENRY. Unless I help you! What can I do?

MR. HOMER. A horse has four feet, and I only have two. I need two more. I'll make a shaggy brown horse suit. I'll be the front end, and you can be the back end. Together we will be one horse. Don't you think that's a wonderful idea?

MR. HENRY. Not exactly! You are forgetting one thing, my friend.

MR. HOMER. What's that?

MR. HENRY. I have never wanted to be a horse.

MR. HOMER. That's because you have never thought about it. Please, as my good friend, do this for me. You may even get to like it. We could get a job as a police horse. You'd get to wear a very handsome saddle.

MR. HENRY. Well . . .

MR. HOMER. Or we could go to work as a farm horse. Think of working in the fields all day getting the sun rather than sitting in an old shop.

MR. HENRY. Well . . .

MR. HOMER. We might even be in a horse show and win a prize. Wouldn't that make you proud?

MR. HENRY. Well . . .

MR. HOMER. Oh, say you'll do it. For me?

MR. HENRY. Well—all right, then. But only because you are my good friend.

(MR. HENRY *starts to work on some leather for the horse's shoes.*)

MR. HOMER. I'll go back to my shop and start working on that shaggy brown cloth I've saved for the horse's suit.

Act 2

Time: That afternoon.
Place: Outside a police station.

MR. HOMER. Now, what will be our name?

MR. HENRY. Henryhomer.

MR. HOMER. Homerhenry. Since I am going to be the Head and you are going to be the Tail, I will always be in front of you. So my name should be in front of yours. That is why we should be called Homerhenry.

(*The two men climb into the shaggy brown horse suit and button it up.* MR. HOMER, *the* HEAD, *stands straight up.* MR. HENRY, *the* TAIL, *stoops over and puts his arms around* MR. HOMER. *A* POLICEMAN *comes out of the police station.* HOMERHENRY *walks over to the* POLICEMAN.)

HEAD. Could you use a police horse?

(*The* POLICEMAN *walks all around* HOMERHENRY, *looking him up and down.*)

POLICEMAN. There is something strange about you, but if you really want to be a police horse, I will give you a try.

(*The* POLICEMAN *gets a saddle and throws it over the back of* HOMERHENRY. HOMERHENRY *sags under the weight of the saddle.*)

TAIL. Oof!

(*The* POLICEMAN *gets up on* HOMERHENRY. HOMERHENRY *sags under the* POLICEMAN'S *weight. The* POLICEMAN'S *feet touch the ground.*)

TAIL. Ugh!

POLICEMAN. Giddap!

(The HEAD moves but the TAIL stays where it is.)

HEAD *(in a soft voice to the TAIL)*. Don't you hear? Giddap! Giddap!

(The TAIL moves but the HEAD stays still. HOMERHENRY, POLICEMAN, and saddle fall.)

POLICEMAN. Oh, this won't do. You are not exactly the police horse I had in mind.

(The POLICEMAN gets up off the ground and goes back to the police station to put the saddle away.)

Act 3

Time: Same afternoon.
Place: A barnyard.

HEAD. Well, we can still get a job on a farm. I'm sure we will make a very fine work horse. Now a farm horse must be able to do exactly as he is told. Listen carefully to the farmer, and when he says, "Giddap!" then you giddap.

TAIL. My back is tired from stooping over so long.

HEAD. Are you ready now?

TAIL. No, I am not ready! I said my back is tired from stooping over so long.

HEAD. Here we go!

TAIL. I tell you my back . . .

HEAD. Here comes the farmer.

(The FARMER *comes out of the barn, and walks all around* HOMERHENRY, *looking him up and down.*)

HEAD. Could you use another farm horse?

FARMER. I could use another horse, but you look a bit strange.

(The TAIL, *tired of stooping, stands up.*)

FARMER. I'm sorry. But unless you can get rid of that hump in your back, I can't use you.

(The HEAD *turns around and looks in surprise.*)

HEAD. That's funny. We had no hump in our back a minute ago.

FARMER. I'm afraid I can't use a horse that's out of shape. You won't do at all.

(The FARMER goes back into the barn. HOMERHENRY goes out through the barnyard gate.)

HEAD. Why did you have to pick that minute to stand up?

TAIL. I told you my back was tired from stooping over so long. I told you three times!

HEAD. Still, you could have waited. There is only one thing left to do. We will try to win a prize at the horse show. Everyone will see that we are a fine-looking horse.

TAIL. To be sure.

HEAD. Only don't stand up. A horse with a hump in its back is not fine-looking.

Act 4

Time: Same afternoon.
Place: A horse show.

(*The* DIRECTOR *runs his hand over* HOMERHENRY's *neck and looks him up and down.*)

DIRECTOR. Can you trot? Can you gallop? In order to win a prize, you must be able to do these things well.

HEAD. Yes.

TAIL. No.

DIRECTOR. Well, which is it?

HEAD. Yes.

TAIL. No.

DIRECTOR. What is the matter with you? Can't you make up your mind?

HEAD. The Head does all the thinking, and I think we can.

DIRECTOR. All right, then. Show me. Trot!

(HOMERHENRY *starts to trot.*)

DIRECTOR. Gallop!

(*The* HEAD *starts to gallop, but the* TAIL *is still in a trot.*)

DIRECTOR. You don't seem to do that very well. I'm sorry, but I can see right away that you would not make a good show horse at all.

(HOMERHENRY *leaves the horse show and goes out on the street.*)

HEAD. I have learned something from all this.

TAIL. And what is that, my friend?

HEAD. I have learned that it is much better to be a good tailor than a bad horse. We will go back to our shops. It is the best thing.

TAIL. To be sure.

(On the way home, the HEAD stops suddenly. The TAIL crashes into the HEAD, and HOMERHENRY falls on his face.)

TAIL. Now what?

(The HEAD reads a billboard sign.)

HEAD. The circus! The circus has come to town. We will become a circus horse!

(HOMERHENRY gallops toward the circus grounds. The back legs can't keep up with the front legs.)

Act 5

Time: Late afternoon.
Place: The circus grounds.

(*The* Circus Manager *is walking around* Homerhenry, *looking him up and down.*)

Circus Manager. What makes you think you would make a good circus horse?

Head. Why, because we are a very different kind of horse.

Circus Manager. You do look a bit strange, but I'll give you a try. The next show is about to begin. Go into the middle ring and show me what you can do.

(Homerhenry *runs into the ring.*)

HEAD. First, we will dance.

(The HEAD lifts his legs and does one kind of dance and the TAIL lifts his legs and does another. People begin to laugh.)

HEAD. Why is everyone laughing at our dance?

TAIL. I'm sure I don't know.

HEAD. Let's try jumping through a ring of fire.

TAIL. F-fire, did you say?

HEAD. Ready? Let's go.

(The HEAD begins to run. The TAIL doesn't budge. People laugh when they see the front part of HOMERHENRY pulling one way and the back part pulling the other way.)

TAIL. I'm not jumping through that ring of fire!

(HOMERHENRY reaches the ring of fire. The HEAD lifts his legs to jump through the fire, but the TAIL doesn't budge.)

TAIL. I said no fire!

HEAD. Oh, all right. No fire. Now what will we do?

TAIL. I don't know. You think of something. This was all your idea to begin with.

(FIRST CLOWN *runs into the ring and jumps on* HOMERHENRY'S *back.* SECOND CLOWN *runs into the ring and does the same thing. Then* THIRD CLOWN *comes in and jumps on* HOMERHENRY'S *neck. The weight is too much for* HOMERHENRY. *He goes limp and falls down. People laugh.*)

CIRCUS MANAGER. You're hired! You will be the funniest act in the whole show. You will go all over the world with my circus.

HEAD. I'm sorry, but I do not wish to be a funny act. I am going home.

TAIL. I'm staying.

(*The* HEAD *begins to move, but the* TAIL *doesn't budge.*)

CIRCUS MANAGER. I have an idea. My circus
comes to this town for one week every
year. Why don't you be a horse just one
week out of the year? The rest of the year
you can be whatever else you like. That
way you will be happy, and I will be happy.

TAIL. That's a fine idea!

HEAD. To be sure.

Act 6

Time: Evening.
Place: Mr. Henry's shop.

MR. HOMER. You won't tell anyone about this, of course.

(MR. HENRY *looks up from his work.*)

MR. HENRY. Tell anyone what?

MR. HOMER. About my wanting to be a horse.

MR. HENRY. Of course not. It is rather silly, a man wanting to be a horse. A tiger, maybe. But not a horse!

MR. HOMER. A tiger?

MR. HENRY. With gold eyes! And black stripes!
The king of the animals!

(*The two men look at each other without
saying anything.*)

MR. HOMER. Bright gold buttons for the eyes!

MR. HENRY. And we could get some straw for
the fur.

MR. HOMER. We'll call him Henryhomer this
time, since it's only right to take turns.

MR. HENRY. To be sure.

Little House in the Big Woods

Laura Ingalls Wilder

About the Story

Long ago, much of our country was a wild land of deep woods, where few people lived. The woman who wrote the next story knew what it was like to grow up in such country in those days. She was born in 1867 in a little log house in the big woods. There she lived the first years of her life with her family —Ma, Pa, Mary, and Carrie.

The little log house stood far away from the next neighbor and even farther away from a town.

Like every family that lived in the wild country in those days, Laura's family had to make, grow, or find almost everything they needed. Pa cut trees into big logs for the house and barn and small logs for the fire. He trapped wild animals for furs, which could be sold for things the family could not make or grow.

Ma made the clothes and did the cooking. She helped take care of the garden and sometimes milked the cow, Sukey.

Everyone in the family had little jobs, or chores, to do. Even little Laura helped Ma set the table and feed the animals.

Life in the big woods was hard. But it was not all work. Like most little girls, Laura, Mary, and Carrie had their dolls. On warm days they played outside. At night Pa told them stories, and they all sang together by the fire.

Living in the big woods was sometimes exciting and even dangerous. Wild animals were never far away. And during the long snowy winter, weeks might go by without the family seeing any other people.

The story that you are about to read began on a spring day, when Laura was five years old. That morning Pa had gone to the town to sell the furs and get things for the family. Ma and the girls had stayed home to take care of the chores. At last it was sundown, and Pa had not yet returned.

Two Big Bears

The sun sank out of sight, the woods grew dark, and he did not come. Ma started supper and set the table, but he did not come. It was time to do the chores, and still he had not come.

Ma said that Laura might come with her while she milked the cow. Laura could carry the lantern.

So Laura put on her coat and Ma buttoned it up. And Laura put her hands into her red mittens that hung by a red yarn string around her neck, while Ma lighted the candle in the lantern.

Laura was proud to be helping Ma with the milking, and she carried the lantern very carefully. Its sides were of tin, with places cut in them for the candle-light to shine through.

When Laura walked behind Ma on the path to the barn, the little bits of candle-light from the lantern leaped all around her on the snow. The night was not yet quite dark. The woods were dark, but there was a gray light on the snowy path, and in the sky there were a few faint stars. The stars did not look as warm and bright as the little lights that came from the lantern.

Laura was surprised to see the dark shape of Sukey, the brown cow, standing at the barnyard gate. Ma was surprised, too.

It was too early in the spring for Sukey to be let out in the Big Woods to eat grass. She lived in the barn. But sometimes on warm days Pa left the door of her stall open so she could come into the barnyard. Now Ma and Laura saw her behind the bars, waiting for them.

Ma went up to the gate, and pushed against it to open it. But it did not open very far, because there was Sukey, standing against it. Ma said,

"Sukey, get over!" She reached across the gate and slapped Sukey's shoulder.

Just then one of the dancing little bits of light from the lantern jumped between the bars of the gate, and Laura saw long, shaggy, black fur, and two little, glittering eyes.

Sukey had thin, short, brown fur. Sukey had large, gentle eyes.

Ma said, "Laura, walk back to the house."

So Laura turned around and began to walk toward the house. Ma came behind her. When they had gone part way, Ma snatched her up, lantern and all, and ran. Ma ran with her into the house, and slammed the door.

Then Laura said, "Ma, was it a bear?"

"Yes, Laura," Ma said. "It was a bear."

Laura began to cry. She hung on to Ma and sobbed, "Oh, will he eat Sukey?"

"No," Ma said, hugging her. "Sukey is safe in the barn. Think, Laura—all those big, heavy logs in the barn walls. And the door is heavy and solid, made to keep bears out. No, the bear cannot get in and eat Sukey."

Laura felt better then. "But he could have hurt us, couldn't he?" she asked.

"He didn't hurt us," Ma said. "You were a good girl, Laura, to do exactly as I told you, and to do it quickly, without asking why."

Ma was trembling, and she began to laugh a little. "To think," she said, "I've slapped a bear!"

Then she put supper on the table for Laura and Mary. Pa had not come yet. He didn't come. Laura and Mary were undressed, and they said their prayers and snuggled into the trundle bed.

Ma sat by the lamp, mending one of Pa's shirts. The house seemed cold and still and strange, without Pa.

Laura listened to the wind in the Big Woods. All around the house the wind went crying as though it were lost in the dark and the cold. The wind sounded frightened.

Ma finished mending the shirt. Laura saw her fold it slowly and carefully. She smoothed it with her hand. Then she did a thing she had never done before. She went to the door and pulled the leather latch-string through its hole in the door, so that nobody could get in from outside unless she lifted the latch. She came and took Carrie, all limp and sleeping, out of the big bed.

She saw that Laura and Mary were still awake, and she said to them: "Go to sleep, girls. Everything is all right. Pa will be here in the morning."

Then she went back to her rocking chair and sat there rocking gently and holding Baby Carrie in her arms.

She was sitting up late, waiting for Pa, and Laura and Mary meant to stay awake, too, till he came. But at last they went to sleep.

In the morning Pa was there. He had brought candy for Laura and Mary, and two pieces of pretty calico to make them each a dress. Mary's was a china-blue pattern on a white ground, and Laura's was dark red with little golden-brown dots on it. Ma had calico for a dress, too; it was brown, with a big, feathery white pattern all over it.

They were all happy because Pa had got such good prices for his furs that he could afford to get them such beautiful presents.

The tracks of the big bear were all around the barn, and there were marks of his claws on the walls. But Sukey and the horses were safe inside.

All that day the sun shone, the snow melted, and little streams of water ran from the icicles, which all the time grew thinner. Before the sun set that night, the bear tracks were only shapeless marks in the wet, soft snow.

After supper Pa took Laura and Mary on his knees and said he had a new story to tell them.

The Story of Pa and the Bear in the Way

"When I went to town yesterday with the furs, I found it hard walking in the soft snow. It took me a long time to get to town, and other men with furs had come in earlier to do their trading. The storekeeper was busy, and I had to wait until he could look at my furs.

"Then we had to bargain about the price of each one, and then I had to pick out the things I wanted to take in trade.

"So it was nearly sundown before I could start home.

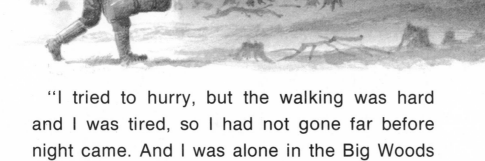

"I tried to hurry, but the walking was hard and I was tired, so I had not gone far before night came. And I was alone in the Big Woods without my gun."

"There were still six miles to walk, and I came along as fast as I could. The night grew darker and darker, and I wished for my gun, because I knew that some of the bears had come out of their winter dens. I had seen their tracks when I went to town in the morning.

"Bears are hungry and cross at this time of year; you know they have been sleeping in their dens all winter long with nothing to eat, and that makes them thin and angry when they wake up. I did not want to meet one.

"I hurried along as quick as I could in the dark. By and by the stars gave a little light. It was still black as pitch where the woods were thick, but in the open places I could see, dimly. I could see the snowy road ahead a little way, and I could see the dark woods standing all around me. I was glad when I came into an open place where the stars gave me this faint light.

"All the time I was watching, as well as I could, for bears. I was listening for the sounds they make when they go carelessly through the bushes.

"Then I came again into an open place, and there, right in the middle of my road, I saw a big black bear.

"He was standing up on his hind legs, looking at me. I could see his eyes shine. I could see his pig-snout. I could even see one of his claws, in the starlight.

"My scalp prickled, and my hair stood straight up. I stopped in my tracks, and stood still. The bear did not move. There he stood, looking at me.

"I knew it would do no good to try to go around him. He would follow me into the dark woods, where he could see better than I could. I did not want to fight a winter-starved bear in the dark. Oh, how I wished for my gun!

"I had to pass that bear, to get home. I thought that if I could scare him, he might get out of the road and let me go by. So I took a deep breath, and suddenly I shouted with all my might and ran at him, waving my arms.

"He didn't move.

"I did not run very far toward him, I tell you!

I stopped and looked at him, and he stood looking at me. Then I shouted again. There he stood. I kept on shouting and waving my arms, but he did not budge.

"Well, it would do me no good to run away. There were other bears in the woods. I might meet one any time. I might as well deal with this one as with another. Besides, I was coming home to Ma and you girls. I would never get here, if I ran away from everything in the woods that scared me.

"So at last I looked around, and I got a good big club, a solid, heavy branch that had been broken from a tree by the weight of snow in the winter.

"I lifted it up in my hands, and I ran straight at that bear. I swung my club as hard as I could and brought it down, bang! on his head.

"And there he still stood, for he was nothing but a big, black, burned stump!"

"I had passed it on my way to town that morning. It wasn't a bear at all. I only thought it was a bear, because I had been thinking all the time about bears and being afraid I'd meet one."

"It really wasn't a bear at all?" Mary asked.

"No, Mary, it wasn't a bear at all. There I had been yelling, and dancing, and waving my arms, all by myself in the Big Woods, trying to scare a stump!"

Laura said: "Ours was really a bear. But we were not scared, because we thought it was Sukey."

Pa did not say anything, but he hugged her tighter.

"Oo-oo! That bear might have eaten Ma and me all up!" Laura said, snuggling closer to him. "But Ma walked right up to him and slapped him, and he didn't do anything at all. Why didn't he do anything?"

"I guess he was too surprised to do anything, Laura," Pa said. "I guess he was afraid, when the lantern shone in his eyes. And when Ma walked up to him and slapped him, he knew *she* wasn't afraid."

"Well, you were brave, too," Laura said. "Even if it was only a stump, you thought it was a bear. You'd have hit him on the head with a club, if he *had* been a bear, wouldn't you, Pa?"

"Yes," said Pa, "I would. You see, I had to."

Old Log House

On a little green knoll
At the edge of the wood,
My great-great-grandmother's
First house stood.

The house was of logs
My grandmother said,
With one big room
And a lean-to-shed.

I like to hear
My grandmother tell
How they built the fireplace
And dug the well.

Forever and ever
I wish I could
Live in a house
At the edge of a wood.

—James S. Tippett

Never Give Up!

A single flower
Pushed right through
A sidewalk crack
So hopeful and strong.

—*Hannah Lyons Johnson*

The Case of the
Silver Fruit Bowl

Donald J. Sobol

"Stay away from Idaville!"

Across the country crooks, big and small, soon got the word. They knew what would happen if they tried anything funny in Idaville — a quick trip to jail. For more than a year, no man, woman, or child had broken a law in Idaville and gotten away with it.

How did Idaville do it? How did it win its war on crime? No one could guess. Idaville looked like any other small town near the sea. It had a park, a library, a bank, a lovely beach, and good places to fish.

And on Spring Street, it had a red house with a garden around it. This was the real headquarters of Idaville's war on crime. For within those red walls lived Encyclopedia Brown.

Encyclopedia's father was chief of the Idaville police. For more than a year now, Chief Brown had been bringing home his hardest cases. Encyclopedia solved them at the dinner table.

Chief Brown wanted to tell the world that his son was a great detective. He wanted to shout,

"My son is the greatest detective who ever walked in sneakers!"

But how could he? Who would believe that the brain behind Idaville's crime cleanup was only ten years old?

Encyclopedia never said a word about the help he gave his father. He didn't want to seem different from any other ten-year-old.

The name Encyclopedia was something else. There was nothing he could do about it. Only his mother, father, and teacher called him by his real name, Leroy. Everyone else called him Encyclopedia.

An encyclopedia is a book or set of books filled with facts from A to Z. So was Encyclopedia's head. You might say he was the only library in the country that could play first base.

One night at dinner, his father ate his soup very slowly. At once, Encyclopedia knew why. Chief Brown had come across a hard case.

Chief Brown put down his spoon. He sat back and said, "Mr. Herman, the owner of the Silver Shop, says he was held up this afternoon."

"*Says?*" Mrs. Brown asked. "You make it sound as if you don't believe him."

"I'm not sure," said Chief Brown, "He says that eight silver dishes were stolen. But no one saw the holdup."

"Why should he be lying?" asked Mrs. Brown.

"Mr. Herman doesn't own the dishes that were stolen. He would not have lost any money because of the holdup," said Chief Brown. "The dishes are Mrs. Edwards'. Mr. Herman was going to try to sell them for her. If he sold them, Mrs. Edwards was to pay him for his time and trouble."

"Do you think he said the dishes were stolen so that he could sell them out of town and keep all the money?" asked Encyclopedia.

"It has been done before, Leroy," said Chief Brown.

"Did Mr. Herman see who held him up?" asked Mrs. Brown.

"One man," said Chief Brown. "Mr. Herman is sure he will know the man if he sees him again."

Chief Brown reached into his shirt pocket and took out a notebook. "I wrote down everything Mr. Herman told me about the holdup," he said. Then he read from his notebook.

"I was alone in the store just after one o'clock. I had my back to the door. I was locking a wall case in which I keep eight fine silver dishes belonging to Mrs. Edwards. I heard the door open. A man's voice said, 'Don't turn around—this is a holdup!' I felt a gun in my back. 'Just hand over everything in the case,' the voice said. After I had given him everything, he left."

Encyclopedia said, "If Mr. Herman had his back to the holdup man all the time, how would he know the man if he saw him again?"

Mrs. Brown looked proudly at Encyclopedia. She was always pleased when he solved a case so quickly.

"Mr. Herman said something else," said Chief Brown. He read again from his notebook.

"The dishes were very shiny. Before I handed over the fruit bowl, I looked inside. I saw the man's face just as if I were looking into a mirror."

Chief Brown put his notebook into his pocket. "You see," he said, "I can't be sure that Mr. Herman is lying."

"Is his store doing well?" asked Encyclopedia.

"No," said Chief Brown. "I called his bank. He has borrowed a lot of money. I think he made up that story about the holdup. With the money he will get from selling the silver out of town, he can give back the money he borrowed."

"You're not being fair," said Mrs. Brown. "Just because Mr. Herman needs money doesn't mean he stole Mrs. Edwards' silver."

"Have you ever seen the shiny silver bowl he used as a mirror, Dad?" asked Encyclopedia.

"Your mother and I nearly bought the bowl last week, as a matter of fact," said Chief Brown. "It's about a foot across and rounded inside like a big spoon."

"We just loved it," said Mrs. Brown. "But we didn't want to spend that much money on a silver bowl."

"I'm happy you didn't," said Encyclopedia.

"Why?" asked Chief Brown.

"Mr. Herman needed the fruit bowl for his story," said Encyclopedia. "He had to say something that showed he acted to get back the silver dishes. So he put in the part about using the fruit bowl as a mirror to see the holdup man's face."

"I'm afraid that part doesn't matter, Leroy," said Chief Brown. "We don't know for sure that he didn't see the man any more than we can know for sure that he made up the rest of the story. We're back where we started."

"Not quite, Dad," said Encyclopedia. "We know that Mr. Herman is lying!"

ARE YOU A GOOD DETECTIVE?
WHAT MADE ENCYCLOPEDIA SURE?

To see how Encyclopedia solved his case,
turn to page 324.

Dina Anastasio

Mary of Valley Forge

The English were the first people to bring their families from Europe to live in America. They cut down the forests and used the logs from the trees to build houses. English ships brought many things they needed to live in the woods. English soldiers stayed to help guard the people.

At first these new families were happy to have help from England. But as the years went by, their feelings toward England began to change.

A time came when most of the people living
in America wanted their own country.
In 1775 America went to war with England
to win the right to be a free country.

George Washington became the head of the
first American Army. For a few years the new
American Army lost more battles than it won.
But then things began to change. Many
people believe the change came in 1778.
General Washington and his men had spent
that winter at a place called Valley Forge.

For the American Army, it was the hardest
winter of the war. Heavy snow kept wagons
from bringing in food. Many soldiers became
sick from cold and hunger.

Many people helped the American Army
get through that long winter at Valley Forge.
One of them was a young girl named Mary
McDonald. This is her story.

One dark snowy morning in the winter of 1778, Mary left her small home with a basket of apples and nuts and set out for Valley Forge. Valley Forge was near Mary's home. But the cold wind and deep snow made the walk seem long.

Mary could not remember such a winter. There had been nothing but snowstorms. The rivers were solid ice. Because of snow and English soliders, the roads to Valley Forge had been closed.

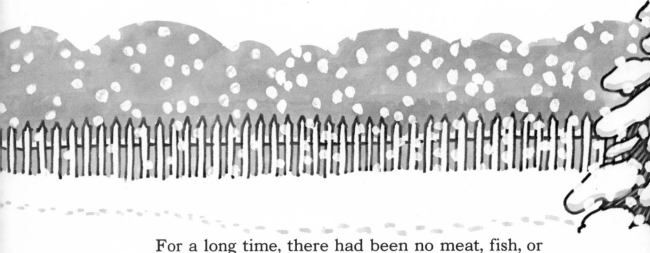

For a long time, there had been no meat, fish, or bread for the soldiers at Valley Forge. Mary had heard people say that the army was sick and hungry. Some said it would not last until spring.

Slowly Mary made her way through the deep snow that covered the parade ground. She tramped by the small log houses, where many American soldiers lay sick, cold, and hungry.

At last she came to a large stone house. It was the headquarters of General George Washington. A tall soldier stood watch at the door. Mary stood by a tree near the house and watched him. His coat was torn and thin.

The soldier saw something move and called out,

"Who goes there?"

Mary was afraid. But she walked over to him and whispered, "May I see General Washington?"

The soldier looked surprised. He asked, "Why do you want to see General Washington?"

Mary could hardly talk. In a small voice she said, "I'd like to join the army."

"Wait here," the soldier said, and he went into the house.

Mary put her cold hands deep into the pockets of her coat and waited. Soon the soldier returned and told her to come with him. He led her inside to a small sitting room, where some ladies were working and talking. A short lady with white hair got up as they came in. She looked down at Mary and smiled.

"I'm told you'd like to join our army," she said.

"Yes," Mary whispered. She was still very afraid.

"How old are you?" the lady asked.

"Almost eight."

"And your name?"

"Mary McDonald."

"Well then, Mary," the lady said, "I'm Mrs. Washington. These women and I are filling baskets with food. When the baskets have been filled, they will be taken to the soldiers."

Mrs. Washington looked at Mary carefully and said, "Maybe you can help. Would you like to take the food to the men?"

"Oh, yes. I would like that," Mary said. "I've brought some food, too." She put the basket of nuts and apples on the table.

"Wonderful," a deep voice from the doorway said.

Mary turned quickly. A tall, very handsome man in a blue coat stood in the doorway.

"Mary," Mrs. Washington said, leading her toward the door. "This is General Washington."

To General Washington she said, "Mary's going to help carry food to the soldiers."

The General smiled. "That's fine," he said. He took Mary to the window, and together they looked out at the snow-covered log houses.

"Many of the men are sick from hunger, Mary," the General told her. "You will be helping them very much."

As they stood by the window, the General started to talk, more to himself than to Mary. "I wonder if spring will ever come," he said. "We can't beat the English without food." Then, with head down, he left the room.

"I belong to the first American Army," Mary thought. "And it is going to be the best army in the whole world."

Spring at Valley Forge

The next morning Mary pulled her coat around her and set out for the stone house. The same tall soldier stood guard by the front door. But this time when he saw her, he smiled.

"Mrs. Washington is waiting for you," he said. Mary ran through the small dark hall and up the stairs. She stood silently by the sitting room door and watched the ladies as they worked. She thought they looked very beautiful.

"Come in, child," Mrs. Washington said.

Mary walked into the room. She put the food which she had brought from home on the table. Then she sat down and waited while the women filled the baskets. Some of their husbands had been hurt in the battles of the past year. Many more of them were very sick from cold and hunger. But when the women talked of spring, there was hope in their voices. The roads would be opened again. They could get the food their husbands needed to become strong again.

When the women had filled their baskets, Mrs. Washington stood and smiled at Mary.

"Now, Mary," she said, giving her two baskets, "take this food to the soldiers."

Mary carried the baskets down the stairs and past the tall soldier, who again smiled at her. She tramped through the deep snow and passed the building where General Washington's gray horse stood waiting. She passed another building where flour and water cakes were baking.

The wind was cold, and the baskets were heavy. But Mary was proud to be part of the American Army. At last she came to a row of log huts and opened the first door.

Mary saw the soldiers lying silently on their beds. A small fire burned in the fireplace at the far end of the log hut. But the room was cold and dark.

Mary walked quietly to the first bed and looked down at the sleeping soldier. The man looked very weak.

"I've brought you some food," Mary whispered.

"So you've brought food," the soldier said in a weak voice. "That's a nice surprise. What's your name?"

"Mary," she answered.

The soldier smiled and said, "Well, Mary, I'm Tom, and I sure can use some food."

Mary gave him some fruit and nuts. He ate quickly while Mary watched. When Tom had finished he said, "That was better than the flour and water cakes we've been living on.

"More snow I see," Tom said sadly, looking at Mary's coat. "Every night I dream that the snow has melted, and the roads have been cleared. I dream that wagons are pulling food through again. And every day I look outside and see snow and more snow."

"Don't worry, Tom," Mary said. "Spring will come. It always does." She touched his hand and moved on. Other soldiers had been waiting silently for food.

Mary gave each soldier some nuts and a little fruit. The men shook her hand and thanked her.

All day long Mary walked through the deep snow carrying baskets of food from General Washington's headquarters to the men in the log huts.

During the next two months, Mary walked many miles carrying baskets from the stone house to the huts. The soldiers looked ahead with pleasure to her visit.

Tuesday was a special day for Mary because that was the day she took food to the hut where Tom lived. Tom had become her special friend. She wished that she could bring him food every day.

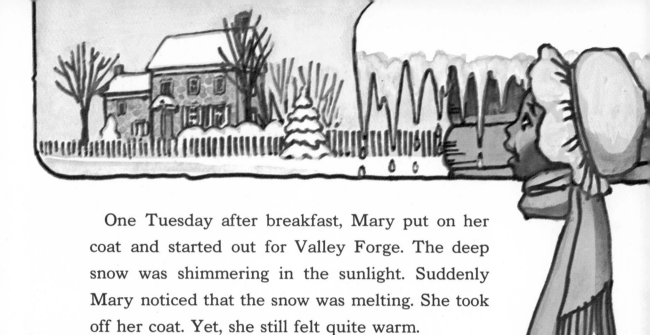

One Tuesday after breakfast, Mary put on her coat and started out for Valley Forge. The deep snow was shimmering in the sunlight. Suddenly Mary noticed that the snow was melting. She took off her coat. Yet, she still felt quite warm.

"*Spring is coming!*" she shouted, as she ran past the guard at the stone house. The guard laughed.

Mrs. Washington and the other ladies were standing by the window when Mary came into the sitting room. They, too, had seen the melting snow. Mary thought they looked really happy for the first time since she had been coming to Valley Forge.

Mary picked up the baskets and hurried through the melting snow to the hut where Tom lived.

"*Spring is here,*" she shouted as she opened the door. Some of the men got up from their beds and walked weakly to the door. When they saw the melting snow and felt the warm air, they shouted with joy.

Tom did not get up. He lay very weak and quiet on his bed. Mary went over to him.

"Please come to the door, Tom," she said. "You will feel better."

Slowly, Tom got up and walked to the door.

"Now you will get better," Mary said.

When Tom felt the warm air and saw the melting snow, he smiled happily and said, "Yes, I know."

Spring brought life and hope to Valley Forge. After the roads had been cleared, wagons came bringing meat and other things the men needed.

When the men were strong enough, they went to the parade ground to drill. For two months, day after day they went there. At last the men were ready for battle again.

One fine day in June, the soldiers marched out of Valley Forge to meet the English. On that day in June, Mary stood on a small hill near the river and watched them pass. Their clothes were torn and thin, but they held their heads proudly as they marched to the music of the beating drums. Some of them saw Mary and waved at her.

At last, Mary saw Tom. His clothes were old. He had no shoes. But he was no longer sick and hungry. When he saw her, he waved. Then he turned and marched off to fight the war.

After the Americans had won the war, they elected George Washington the first president of their new country. President Washington never forgot the winter that his brave army spent at Valley Forge. And Mary was always proud to have been part of it. She never forgot that she had once met our first president.

George Washington's Breakfast

Jean Fritz

George W. Allen was proud of two things—
his name and his birthday. George was named
for George Washington, and he had the same
birthday. It made him want to know everything
there was to know about George Washington.

Already he knew quite a lot. He knew that
Washington was a general and lived in Mount
Vernon and was our first President.

Then one day George W. Allen thought of something he didn't know. George's mother and father had gone off to work, and his grandmother was cooking eggs.

"Grandma," George said, "what did George Washington eat for breakfast?"

"How should I know?" said his grandmother. "That was before my time. And don't think that I'm going to help you find out, either!"

George's grandmother knew what George was like. Whenever he wanted to find out something, he just couldn't rest until he did. And he didn't let anyone else rest either. He did just what his grandfather used to do—ask questions, collect books, and pester everyone for answers. And George's grandmother wasn't going to fool around now about breakfasts that were over and done with so many years ago.

"Well," George said, "if I find out, will you cook me George Washington's breakfast?"

George's grandmother looked at the clock on the wall. "George, you'll be late for school," she said.

"But will you?" George asked. "Will you cook me George Washington's breakfast?"

George's grandmother was still looking at the clock.

"I'll cook anything," she said, "if you hurry."

After school that day George went right to the library. Miss Willing, the lady in charge, smiled when she saw George come in. "I wonder what that Allen boy wants to know now," she thought.

"Miss Willing," said George, "do you know what George Washington ate for breakfast?"

Miss Willing could hardly remember what she'd had for breakfast that morning. But like George, she liked to find out answers.

Together George and Miss Willing went to the encyclopedia and looked under *W.* "Washington, George." The encyclopedia said that he was born in 1732, married in 1759, was elected President in 1789, and died in 1799. It told about his trips and the battles he fought. But it didn't say what he ate for breakfast.

Miss Willing showed George where to find the books about George Washington. George picked out four of them to take home, and Miss Willing promised that she would read some of the rest.

That night after supper, George gave his father and mother each a book to read.

"Don't look at me," his grandmother said. "I said I'd cook, but I won't look."

So George kept the other two books for himself. But not one of the books said anything about what Washington ate for breakfast.

Day after day George, his mother and father, and Miss Willing read. Then one day Miss Willing said they had read all the books about Washington.

Then George had a good idea. "Let's go to Washington's home in Mount Vernon where his breakfasts were cooked."

The next weekend George and Mr. and Mrs. Allen got into the car and started out for Mount Vernon. It was a long trip. When they got there, George and his mother and father went right to the kitchen. They walked on the same path that Washington had walked on. Every time George Allen put his feet down, he thought of George Washington's feet in the same place.

The kitchen was at the side of the house. It was a large room with a big fireplace at one end and lots of pots and pans at the other. George held his breath. It was at that very fireplace that Washington's breakfasts had been cooked.

George turned to a guard standing at the door. "Can you tell me," George said, "what George Washington ate for breakfast?"

The guard answered, "Breakfast was at 7:00. People were given cold meats and tea."

"And did George Washington eat the same breakfast?" George asked.

"I don't know," said the guard. "I've only been here eight weeks."

On Sunday George and his mother and father went home. George's grandmother and Miss Willing were waiting for them.

"No luck," George said to them.

Mr. Allen put his hand on George's shoulder. "It was a good try, son. You can't win them all."

"Sometimes there's nothing to do but give up," Mrs. Allen said.

"Give up?"

"I can't give up!" George shouted. "George Washington's men didn't have enough to eat during the war, and they didn't give up. What do you think I am?"

George was so mad, he went up to the attic and closed the door. It was quiet up there.

The Book in the Attic

In the attic was a box filled with things George guessed his grandmother was going to throw away. On top of the box was an old stuffed dog. He remembered that dog. His name was Homer. One ear was ripped now. George put him aside.

George looked back in the box and saw some old comics. It was a good thing he'd come up here, he thought. No one should throw away old comics. Under the comics George found a very old book. It must have been his grandfather's.

He found a part on George Washington and began to read. "Washington breakfasts about 7:00 on . . ." George let out a yell, took the book, and ran out of the attic.

"Grandma!" he shouted. "George Washington breakfasts about 7:00 on three small Indian hoecakes and tea!"

"George," said his grandmother. "I don't have any idea what an Indian hoecake is."

George went to the dictionary. He looked under *H.* "Hoecake. A cake of cornmeal and water and salt baked before an open fire on a hoe."

"I've cornmeal and water and salt," said Grandma. "I guess I can make some Indian hoecakes."

George's father made a fire in the fireplace, and George's mother filled the kettle with water for the tea.

George said he was going to look for a hoe, but his grandmother stopped him. "You don't want me to cook those things on a hoe, do you?" she asked.

"Well, that's what the dictionary says," said George.

George's grandmother looked in the dictionary. "The dictionary means that a hoe was used when hoecakes were first made. I think hoecakes were around a long time before Washington. Did you see a hoe in George Washington's kitchen in Mount Vernon?" she asked.

George said he hadn't seen one.

"Then we'll use what we have," said Grandma. She mixed the cornmeal and water and salt in a bowl and then made little cakes.

Soon the tea kettle began to steam and the hoecakes began to turn a nice golden brown.

George Washington's breakfast was ready at last.

George took a bite of hoecake. It was pretty good, he thought. He looked at his mother and father and his grandmother and Miss Willing all eating hoecakes together on a Sunday afternoon. George felt closer to Washington than he'd ever felt in his whole life. It was as if George Washington were there at the fireplace with them.

But when George finished his three small hoecakes and his tea, he was still hungry. And if he was hungry, what about Washington? For a man who was six feet tall and the Father of His Country, it wasn't much of a breakfast.

"I hope Washington didn't have long to wait for lunch," George said. "I hope he had a nice big lunch waiting for him. I wonder what . . ."

"George Washington Allen," his grandmother cried. "Don't you say another word."

"Not today," Miss Willing said. "The library is closed today."

"Okay," said George. "Not today."

Look It Up!

Sue, Bill, Jack, and Mary are all looking for facts about cornmeal. Sue is looking at a dictionary. Bill is looking at an encyclopedia. Jack is looking at a cookbook. Mary is looking at the glossary in *Never Give Up!*

Who is trying to find out what part of speech *cornmeal* is?

Who is trying to find out what *cornmeal* means in "George Washington's Breakfast"?

Who is trying to find out how much cornmeal to use in making hoecakes?

Who is trying to find out how much cornmeal is made in the United States each year?

Mummy Slept Late and
Daddy Fixed Breakfast

Daddy fixed breakfast.
He made us each a waffle.
It looked like gravel pudding.
It tasted something awful.

"Ha, ha," he said, "I'll try again.
This time I'll get it right."
But what I got was in between
Bituminous and anthracite.

"A little too well done? Oh well,
I'll have to start all over."
That time what landed on my plate
Looked like a manhole cover.

The next time Dad gets breakfast
When Mummy's sleeping late,
I think I'll skip the waffles.
I'd sooner eat the plate!

—John Ciardi

How to Keep the Cousin You Hate from Spending a Whole Weekend at Your House and Maybe Even Longer...

Bernice Myers

Your mother is talking to
your aunt on the telephone.
She has just invited
the cousin you hate the most
to spend the weekend.

Don't get upset. And
don't try the one
where you throw yourself
on the floor,
roll around holding your neck,
and kick your arms and legs.
It won't work.

Since your mother
has lived with you
all your life, she knows
all your little tricks.

So wait until she is off
the telephone.
After she reminds you
to be polite and to let
your cousin do anything he likes
because he is the guest,
begin taking the pictures
down from the wall.

Remind your mother
that your cousin likes to
play handball, and you wouldn't
want the ball to crash into
any of her pictures.

That will surely give
your mother and father
something to think about.
But don't stop.
Keep building it up.

When you're asked to make the
bed for your cousin,
start making up the crib.
If your father asks questions,
say that your cousin always
sleeps in the crib at night
with your little brother.

By now your mother and father
are talking very quietly
somewhere where you can't hear.

Quickly gather up all the pillows
you can find and drop them
all over the floor in your
bedroom.

Be ready for more questions. Just
say that you don't want your cousin
to hurt himself if he falls
while he's sleep-walking.

That should get your mother
back on the telephone to your aunt.

But if it doesn't and
your cousin comes for the weekend
anyway, then remember he is
your guest.

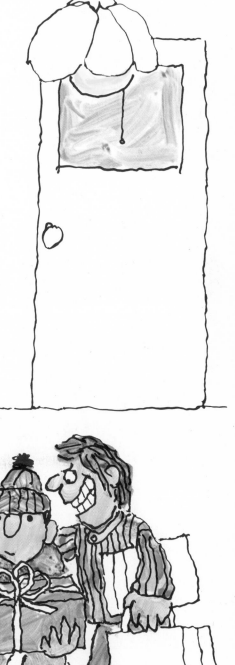

Where the Good Luck Was

Osmond Molarsky

The day Arnold got out of the hospital, his
three best friends were sitting on his front
stairs. They were waiting for him to come home.

"How come you're walking on crutches?"
Jackson said. "We thought you were well."

"I have to walk on crutches for three months,"
Arnold said. "My leg got broken good."

"Next time maybe you won't jump off a roof
with an umbrella," Rudy said.

"How come you're using those old wooden crutches?" Kevin asked. "You should have aluminum crutches."

"They cost twenty-four dollars and fifty cents," Arnold said. "The hospital lent me these wooden crutches. Anyway, who needs them? Watch this." Arnold swung his feet up in front, then up in back, galloped off to the corner, and back again. "I've got the fastest crutches in the West," he said. "Anyone want to race me?"

None of his friends wanted to race him. They were thinking.

Then Kevin said, "Arnold should have some shiny aluminum crutches. A kid on our block with aluminum crutches — that would be cool."

"How would you like that, Arnold?" Jackson asked.

"That's okay with me," Arnold said.

"Let's start an Arnold McWilliams Aluminum Crutches Fund and get him some," said Kevin.

"How do we get the money?" Rudy asked.

"Easy," Jackson said. But he wasn't really sure.

Just then Lucky came tearing around the corner, carrying a long stick. Lucky was always finding things. Once, a long time ago, he found a new Boy Scout knife. After that, he always walked with his head down, so he wouldn't miss anything on the ground.

"What's up, Lucky?" said Jackson.

"Who's got some gum?" Lucky asked. Lucky was excited. "You know the sidewalk grating in front of the toy store? I saw a quarter down there!" he said. "With some gum on the end of this stick, I could get it. Who has some gum?"

Jackson said, "I have a piece in my pocket. For three cents, I'll let you use it."

"Three cents!" Lucky said. "For ten cents I could get a whole pack!"

"Wait a minute," said Kevin. "We're starting a fund to buy Arnold aluminum crutches. How about if Jackson gives the gum to Lucky, and Lucky gives the quarter to the fund?"

"What's the matter with wooden crutches?" Lucky asked.

"A kid on our block with real aluminum crutches would be cool," said Jackson.

Lucky tried to think why Arnold shouldn't have aluminum crutches, but he couldn't. "Okay," he said. "I'll give the quarter if Jackson gives me the gum."

"You know what?" said Kevin. "I bet there are fifty gratings around here. We could get money for the fund out of all of them."

"Let me have the gum," Lucky said. He put the gum on the end of his stick and put the stick down through the grating. He tried many times before he touched the quarter with the gum. He pushed down on it, to make it stick. But when he pulled the stick up, the quarter fell off.

"I've got an idea," said Kevin. "Rudy, give me your magnet." Rudy handed his magnet to Kevin. "Who's got some string?" Kevin asked.

"Here," said Jackson, and in a minute Kevin was letting the magnet down on the end of the string. At last the magnet touched the quarter. Kevin began to pull the magnet up. Nothing was on it but an old nail that had been next to the quarter.

"Boy, are we silly," Kevin said. "I just remembered. A magnet picks up iron and steel. A quarter isn't made up of iron or steel."

"There has got to be a way to get money out of gratings," Kevin said.

Just then Mr. M. B. Pendleton walked by the boys. "What are you boys doing?" he asked.

"We were trying to get that quarter up from the grating," Lucky said. "But it won't work."

"A quarter?" said the old man.

"We need it to buy aluminum crutches for Arnold. He has a broken leg," said Kevin.

"How would you like to make a little money for the crutches?" asked Mr. Pendleton.

"How?" asked Rudy.

"My attic is full of junk I want to throw away — old newspapers, old clothes, old books," said the old man. "I'll pay you kids fifty cents an hour to carry it out to the sidewalk for the garbage man."

"Does each of us get fifty cents an hour?" Jackson wanted to know. "Or is that for all of us?"

"Fifty cents an hour for all of you," the old man said.

"Wait a minute," said Jackson, and he got all his friends together. They whispered for a minute. Then he said, "We want twenty cents an hour for each of us."

"All right," said Mr. Pendleton. "Come with me."

"I'm staying here to get that quarter," said Lucky.

"Good luck, Lucky," said Kevin, and off the boys went with Mr. Pendleton.

The Leather Box

The houses on the old man's block were big and tall. But the biggest of all was the house of Mr. M. B. Pendleton. The boys had seen it, but they had never been inside it.

"Here we are," said the old man. He took out his big key ring and let them into the house. He led them up to the attic.

All over the attic were old tables, lamps, and piles of newpapers. There were boxes with writing on them that said *Books, Mary's Wedding Dress, Peter's Football.* There was even a small box marked *Rags.* Kevin picked it up and thought it was very heavy for a box of rags.

The boys went up and down the stairs like ants, carrying bundles and putting them on the sidewalk. In less than three hours, the job was done.

"That makes me feel much better. How much do I owe you?" asked Mr. Pendleton.

"We started at one o'clock," Jackson said. "Now it's five minutes to four."

"Let's call it three hours," the old gentleman said. "At twenty cents an hour for three boys, that makes it sixty cents for each hour. Three hours is a dollar and eighty cents. I'll make it two dollars even." He gave the boys the money.

"Now all we need is twenty-two dollars and fifty cents more," Jackson said, as the boys walked away.

"Listen," said Kevin. "Remember how heavy that little box was that was marked *Rags?*"

"Yes," said Jackson.

"I'm going to look inside it," Kevin said.

The boys watched as Kevin opened the box. "Those are rags, all right," Jackson said.

"Rags can't be that heavy," Kevin said. He reached in and pulled out some rags. Under them was a leather box. Kevin lifted the lid.

"It's nothing but some old silver," said Kevin.

"I thought it might be worth something," said Rudy.

Kevin lifted out a silver spoon. It was a beautiful shape. "Maybe if we shine the silver it might be worth a lot of money," he said. "We could sell it."

"We can't sell it. It belongs to Mr. Pendleton," Rudy said.

"He told us to take it away," said Jackson. "It's just like we found them. Finders, keepers! The garbage truck would have come and taken the box."

"I think we should tell Mr. Pendleton," Rudy said.

Kevin picked up the black box, and the boys went up the steps and knocked on the door.

Mr. Pendleton opened the door. "Yes?" he said.

Kevin showed him the box. The old man looked at the silver. "This belonged to my grandmother," he said.

"Did you mean to throw it away?" Jackson asked. "It was in a box that said *Rags*. We put the box out with the rest of the stuff."

"Boys," Mr. Pendleton said, "you have done me a very good turn. This silver is worth a lot to me. You should have something in return. What do you think it should be?"

Suddenly a thought came to Jackson. "Twenty-two dollars and fifty cents," he said.

"If that is what you want, that is what you will get," said Mr. Pendleton. He took out his billfold and gave the boys exactly twenty-two dollars and fifty cents.

The boys thanked Mr. Pendleton and hurried to the store to get the new crutches.

Inside the store, Jackson said to the clerk, "We'd like to look at some aluminum crutches. They're for him," and he looked at Arnold.

"Yes," said the clerk, and he brought out some crutches. "There you are young man. Try them."

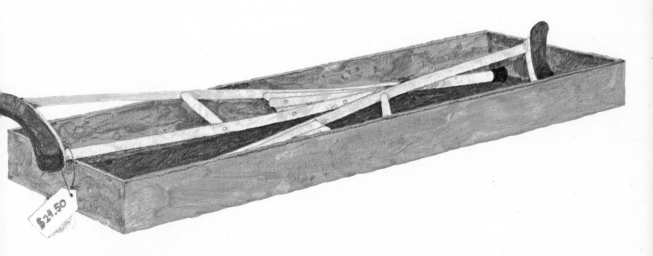

Arnold walked up and down. "They are nice and light," he said. Then he swung his feet up in the air. He sat down hard. His friends picked him up. "That hurt," he said.

"What did you think you were doing?" said
the clerk. "Crutches are not to do tricks on."

"Aluminum ones aren't. I can see that," said
Arnold. "I'll stick to wooden crutches."

Everyone was disappointed. No boy on their
block would have aluminum crutches. And what
would they do with the twenty-four dollars and
fifty cents in the Arnold McWilliams Aluminum
Crutches Fund?

Arnold could see that his friends were
disappointed. He tried to think how he could
make it up to them. "Remember the hospital
lent me these crutches until I get well," he said.
"I've got an idea. They have plenty of crutches
but no aluminum ones."

"I get it," said Rudy. "We can give the
aluminum crutches to the hospital."

"Right," said Arnold. "Just what I was thinking. On the crutches it could say

Given by the
Arnold McWilliams Aluminum
Crutches Fund."

"How do we put that on the crutches?" asked Arnold.

"We can get a name tape and stick it on. My dad had one made for his fishing pole. It cost a quarter," said Kevin.

The boys ran back to the store, bought the crutches, and went to get the name tape made.

Suddenly Rudy stopped. "We have no quarter," he said. "We spent all the money on the crutches."

"Follow me," said Jackson. In less than two minutes they were in front of the store where Lucky was fishing through the grating again.

"Any luck?" asked Jackson.

"No," said Lucky. "I got the quarter, okay. But I dropped my Scout knife down there, and I can't get it up."

"Too bad," said Jackson. "We made twenty-four dollars and fifty cents. We've bought the crutches already."

Lucky could hardly believe it. Twenty-four dollars and fifty cents! But there were the crutches right before his eyes.

"We need a quarter," Jackson said, "for a name tape. We're giving the crutches to the hospital."

"You can't have the quarter," Lucky said. He had lost his knife trying to get the quarter, and he wasn't going to give it up.

"Okay, then," said Jackson. "Rudy won't pull up your knife with his magnet."

"Get the knife first," Lucky said. "Then I'll give you the quarter."

Rudy got the magnet and string out of his pocket. He pulled the knife through the grating.

"Thanks," Lucky said. "My luck is sure with me."

The boys raced off to the store and made the name tape. The tape said,

The Arnold McWilliams Alumum Crutches Fund.

Kevin left out the *in* in *aluminum*. But the people at the hospital were very glad to get the crutches.

It had been a lucky day — even for Lucky.

241

Fidelia

Ruth Adams

Almost everyone in Fidelia's family played an instrument. Her Papa played the trumpet with a band. The band played at dances and the annual Mexican-American picnic. Fidelia was proud of how well her father played his trumpet.

Fidelia's brother and sister played in the school orchestra. Her brother, Alberto, played the trombone, and her sister, Carmela, played the clarinet. The orchestra played for P.T.A. meetings, and once a year the best players were picked to be in the All City Orchestra.

Fidelia didn't play anything.

"You will have to wait," said Papa. "I don't have the money to get another instrument right now."

"Your arms aren't long enough to play a trombone," said Alberto.

"You need all your front teeth to play the clarinet," said Carmela.

Fidelia didn't want to play the trombone or the clarinet. She wanted to play the violin.

One morning Fidelia stopped by the music room while the orchestra was practicing. Up and down went Miss Toomey's baton. Fidelia listened to the sounds of the violins. She closed her eyes so she could hear the music better. She started to move closer until she heard a loud crash. She opened her eyes to find that she had knocked over a big drum. Everyone stopped playing and looked at Fidelia.

"What have we here?" asked Miss Toomey.

"That's our sister, Fidelia," said Carmela. "She wants to play in the orchestra."

"Fidelia, come here," said Miss Toomey. "What instrument do you want to play?"

"The violin," whispered Fidelia.

"You're a bit young to play the violin," said Miss Toomey. "But, we need someone to play the tom-tom for the Indian Dance we are practicing. Would you like to try?"

"Yes, thank you," said Fidelia.

The tom-tom didn't have the same beautiful sound as the violin. Still, Fidelia did her best. She listened to the beat of the music. She watched Miss Toomey's baton. She learned to start on the downbeat, and she learned how to tell when to stop. But she wished that she could play a violin.

One morning Miss Toomey said, "Boys and girls, Mrs. Reed is coming next week to pick the best players for the All City Orchestra."

Everyone began to talk at once. Miss Toomey called for order.

The orchestra began to practice the Indian Dance. Fidelia beat her tom-tom with a heavy heart. What could she play for Mrs. Reed? If only she had a violin. Then Fidelia had an idea.

On her way home from school, she stopped at a candy store and asked the lady for a small box. The lady found one with a lid that was just right.

Down the street, a new building was going up. Fidelia saw a pile of wood and found a board that looked about right. "Please, may I have this board?" she asked one of the men.

"Take the whole pile if you want it," said the man.

"No, thank you," said Fidelia. "I just want one."

Back home, Fidelia took the box and the board into the garage. She found a hammer and a can filled with nails and tried to nail the lid to the sides of the box. But the nails slid through the board and stuck out. They did not touch the sides of the box at all.

Just then Alberto came into the garage. "What are you doing?" he asked.

"I'm making something," she said. She quickly hid the box and board behind her back.

Alberto looked over Fidelia's shoulder and said, "You need some braces."

He took the hammer and nailed three pieces of wood to the ends of the lid and the middle of the box. Then he nailed the board onto the box. Fidelia watched.

"What's next?" Alberto asked.

"Strings," said Fidelia. "What can I use for strings and pegs?"

"Well, rubber bands for the strings, I think," said Alberto. "But I don't know what to do about pegs. I guess we'll just have to use nails."

"Carmela has a collection of rubber bands," said Fidelia. "I'll go ask her for some."

Fidelia got four rubber bands from Carmela. Alberto nailed four nails at each end of the board on the box to hold them.

Fidelia plucked the rubber bands. "It sounds awful!" she cried.

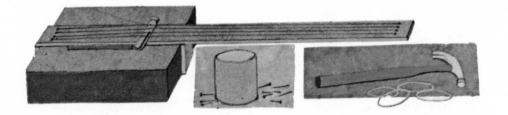

Carmela came into the garage. "If you are trying to make a violin, you need a bridge for the strings to go over. I'll be right back," she said.

Carmela returned with a clothespin. She slid it under the rubber bands. "Now see if you can play a tune," she told Fidelia.

Fidelia placed the violin under her chin and plucked it with the fingers of her right hand. With the fingers of her left hand, she pushed down on the rubber bands.

As Alberto and Carmela left the garage, Fidelia thanked them for helping her. Then she began to practice playing her violin. By dinner time the ends of her fingers hurt. But she knew exactly how to make the sounds she wanted.

A Beginning

The day came for Mrs. Reed to pick the players for the All City Orchestra. Fidelia put her violin into a bag and went to school.

As Fidelia opened the door to the music room, Carmela whispered, "Hurry up! We are going to play the Indian Dance first. Mrs. Reed is already here."

Fidelia put her bag in the corner and got the tom-tom. She watched Miss Toomey. She counted carefully. She played her very best.

Miss Toomey said, "Next, we will play a quiet song."

That was what Fidelia had been waiting for. Quietly she took her violin out of the bag. When she heard the violins, she began to play.

Suddenly Fidelia saw that everyone else had stopped playing. They were all looking at her. She felt hot all over.

"Fidelia, come up here," said Miss Toomey. "What is this?"

"It's a violin that Alberto helped me make," Fidelia answered.

Mrs. Reed held out her hand. "Was this your own idea?" she asked Fidelia.

"Yes," answered Fidelia.

"It was a good idea," said Mrs. Reed, "but I'm afraid you cannot play a tune on this violin."

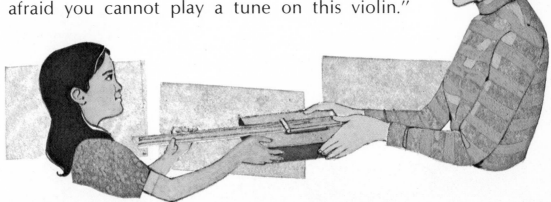

"Oh, but I can play a tune," cried Fidelia. "I've been practicing. I'll show you."

Fidelia plucked away at the rubber bands. When she finished playing, Mrs. Reed asked, "How did you know where to place your fingers on the strings?"

"I watched the others," said Fidelia.

"Would you like to play a real violin?" Mrs. Reed asked.

"Oh, yes! But I am too little," said Fidelia.

Mrs. Reed went out of the room and came back with the smallest violin case any of the children had ever seen. As she opened the case she said, "This is a quarter-size violin, boys and girls. Let's see how it fits Fidelia."

It fit Fidelia exactly right.

"Fidelia," said Mrs. Reed, "the boy who used this violin needs a larger size, so I am going to leave it here for you to use. Miss Toomey will start you in the beginning string class. I will come back in a few weeks to see how you are doing."

Fidelia put the little violin under her chin. She set the bow on the strings. "I'm ready, Miss Toomey," she said.

"Beginning string class meets after lunch, Fidelia. You'll have to wait," said Miss Toomey.

Alberto played his trombone and Carmela played her clarinet in the All City Orchestra, but Fidelia didn't mind. She had a violin exactly her size, and she was in the beginning string class.

Everyone has to start somewhere.

WORD PICTURES

The way you use words depends on what you are trying to do. Below are two ways to write about a sunrise. Which one might be written by a weatherman? Which one was written by the poet, Emily Dickinson?

The sun rose at 6:15 A.M.

I'll tell you how the sun rose
A ribbon at a time.

Which of these sentences paint a word picture? Which ones tell a fact?

Mama was angry.
There was fire in Mama's eyes.

Arnold had the fastest crutches in the west.
Arnold moved fast on his crutches.

The Pink Suit

Marilyn Hirsh

Eugene was eating when Mother came in with a big box.

"Such a bargain I got," she said. "You won't believe it."

"I don't believe it," said Eugene. *"A pink suit!* What will the kids say? I won't wear it!"

"Do you think suits grow on trees? I can't return it. So you'll wear it," said Mother.

The next day began, as always, with Mother talking to herself. This time it was about a son who didn't know how lucky he was to have a new suit.

So Eugene wore his new suit.

At the end of the block all his friends were playing stickball. Eugene made a sharp turn around the corner.

He tried to get lost in the crowd. But it seemed that everyone was looking at him.

Eugene thought he'd better leave his neighborhood. He wanted to go where no one knew him.

He walked and walked. He found new places where he felt at home.

"That's a beautiful suit, young man," said the flower seller. "Just like one of my flowers." Eugene did not say thank you.

Eugene was tired of walking so he ducked into the movies. He spent the rest of the day there until he knew the movie by heart.

When it was dark, Eugene went home. He was so happy not to be noticed that he forgot to be scared.

He was sent to bed for being late. All night Eugene dreamed of ways of getting rid of the pink suit.

The next day Eugene's neighborhood was having a street party. Everyone for blocks around was invited. And they all came in their best clothes.

Eugene did not look for his friends in the crowd. He went to watch the dancing and saw a big fat lady in a big pink dress. Eugene followed her everywhere.

The lady helped herself to some food, and so did Eugene. As they reached for the cake, the lady spilled her tea all over Eugene.

Gladly Eugene took the suit to the cleaner's.

Sadly he went to pick it up.

But it wasn't there. They sent him to the lost and found. The man said, "Go over to the boys' clothes rack and see if you can find your suit."

Another boy was there. "I found my suit," he said, "but I still hate it."

"I hate mine, too," said Eugene. "I could see it from across the room."

"Yours isn't so bad," said the boy.

"Let's trade," said Eugene.

"I bet nobody else has a pink suit," said the boy.

"I bet you're right," said Eugene.

Company Clothes

I had to dress up
and not wear jeans
or even my comfortable
in-betweens,
and not wear boots
or my zebra sweater
because Mother said
she'd had a letter
and someone she knew
when she was small
was stopping to call
so I had to look better.

And what do you know!
Their boy was John…
And he had jeans
and a sweater on!
So I changed mine back
in one-two-three,
to keep my company
company.

—Aileen Fisher

259

The Talking Leaves

Bernice Kohn

A long time ago, when the United States was young, there lived an Indian boy named Sequoyah. He was not as tall as his friends, and he was lame. Yet this small lame boy grew up to be the greatest Cherokee of them all. For it was Sequoyah who solved the mystery of the talking leaves.

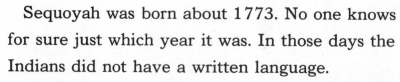

Sequoyah was born about 1773. No one knows for sure just which year it was. In those days the Indians did not have a written language.

Sequoyah's grandfather was a great chief, and his mother was a princess. Sequoyah's father was a white man. He was a soldier and a trader. The Cherokees liked him so much that they let him marry their princess. And they gave him an island to live on.

When Sequoyah was a baby, his father had to go back to his own people. Sequoyah and his mother stayed with the tribe.

As a boy, Sequoyah hurt his leg. He became very sick and almost died. He got well, but his leg was always weak after that. He began to hunt less and to make more use of his strong hands.

Sequoyah started to paint, and soon he could make the masks the men in his tribe wore. Later he learned to make strong iron pots for his mother.

By the time Sequoyah was a young man, he was able to make beautiful necklaces and rings. When he married, he built a log hut and a spinning wheel with his own hands for his young Cherokee wife.

Sequoyah and his wife had five children. First four sons were born, and then a daughter.

In 1812 Sequoyah heard that the United States was at war with England. He left his family to fight with the American soldiers.

In camp the food and clothes of the soldiers were strange to Sequoyah. But the thing he found most strange was their language, English.

Then Sequoyah found out something that was to change his life and the life of the whole Cherokee tribe. Sequoyah found out about reading and writing.

One day Sequoyah saw a soldier with something that looked like a large white leaf. It was a piece of paper. The "leaf" was covered with many black marks. He watched the soldier as he looked at the "leaf." The soldier shook his head and said, "We will just see about that!" To Sequoyah it seemed as though the little marks written on the paper were *talking* to the soldier.

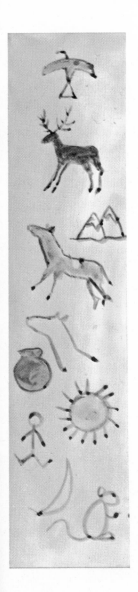

When the war was over, Sequoyah was very happy to return to his tribe. He had missed his family and friends. Still, Sequoyah had not forgotten the mystery of the talking leaves. He made up his mind that if leaves could talk, then he would make them talk for the Cherokee people.

Sequoyah tried to make a picture sign for every word he could think of. He made the signs on pieces of bark. He made picture signs for horses and colts and pots and every other thing he knew. In a very short time, he had so many signs no one could remember them all. Even Sequoyah was getting mixed up. There had to be a better way.

Sequoyah thought and thought, and then one day the idea came. Of course! All words are made up of sounds. He didn't need a sign for every word but only one for every sound. By putting the sounds together, he could make any word.

Sequoyah set to work right away to find out how many sounds there were in the Cherokee language. He said each sound out loud. His friends began to look at him strangely.

Then Sequoyah found a book written in English. Maybe from it he could learn the magic of the talking leaves. He would write some of the letters on pieces of bark. A few of them looked better upside down or on their sides, so he made them that way.

Sequoyah worked night and day. The pile of bark grew higher and higher. But Sequoyah didn't care about anything else.

Some of the Cherokees could not understand what Sequoyah was doing. They began to talk against him. One said that Sequoyah was making bad magic for the tribe. Sequoyah's wife became angry at Sequoyah. She picked up all the bark and threw it in the fire.

At first Sequoyah was very upset, but he started to work all over again. At last Sequoyah was finished. He had made a sign for each of the syllables in the Cherokee language. Sequoyah had made a syllabary.

A syllabary has a sign for every syllable. There were eighty-six signs in Sequoyah's syllabary.

a D eR iT oᏠ uᏋ vi

Ꮝga Ꮕka Ꮧge Ᏹgi A go Ꭷgu Egv
Ꮦha Ᏼhe Ꮥhi Ꮟho Ꮧho Ꮶhv
Wla Ꮪle Ꮅli Ꮐlo Mlu Ꮑlv
Ꮉma Ꭴme Hmi �ismo Ᵽmu
Ꮎna Ꮃhna Gnah Ꭰne Ꮒni Zno Ꮕnu Ꮗhv
Ꮖqua Ꮖque Ꮗqui Ꮖquo Ꮗquu Ꮗquv
Ꮋs Usa Ꮄse bsi Ꮏso Ꮫsu Rsv
Ꮈda Wta Ꮪde Ꮦte Ꮧdi Ꮧti Ꮩdo Sdu Ᵽdv
Ꮸdla Ꮭtla Ꮅtle Ꮳtli Ᏺtlo Ᏼtlu Ptlv
Ꮳtsa Ꮸtse Ꮧtsi Ꮪtso Ꮪtsu Ꮯtsv
Ꮹwa Ꮺwe Ꮻwi Ꮼwo Ꮽwu Ꮾwv
Ꮿya Ᏸye Ᏹyi Ꮒhyo Ᏻgyu Ᏼyv

But now what? Could other Cherokees learn to use the syllabary? His little daughter could already read it and write it. But what about the others? Would they care? Would they *want* to learn?

Sequoyah thought the time had come to find out if all the years of hard work had been worth it. It was 1821, and it was time to make a test.

The Test

Sequoyah went to the head of the Cherokee tribe, and a meeting was called. Word of Sequoyah's talking leaves went through the tribe. The meeting room was soon filled with excited people.

Sequoyah was sent out of the room with two guards. They made sure that Sequoyah could not hear what was happening in the room.

Inside, the chiefs gave messages to Sequoyah's daughter. Nothing could be heard in the room but the little girl's quill pen as she quickly began writing the messages.

At last Sequoyah was called back into the room. He took the paper from his daughter's hand and read the messages in a clear, loud voice. It worked! The Cherokee people had a written language!

Now everyone wanted to learn the new syllabary at once. Little children and wise old men worked together to learn it.

During the next year Sequoyah helped show many Cherokees how to teach the syllabary. By 1828 the Cherokee people had their own newspaper and books and schools. Cherokee children could learn to read and write.

Of course, everyone was very proud of Sequoyah, not just the Cherokees but the whole country. Never before had just one man made up a written language by himself. Even the President of the United States heard of what Sequoyah had done. To show how proud he was of Sequoyah, he gave him a gift of $500.00 a year for the rest of his life.

But what pleased Sequoyah most was a beautiful silver medal with his picture on it. It was given to him by his own people. He wore the medal around his neck for the rest of his life.

When Sequoyah heard about some Cherokees in Mexico, he wondered if they could use the syllabary, too. He made up his mind to go and look for them.

Sequoyah set out for Mexico in 1842. It was a long and hard trip on foot and on horseback, much too hard a trip for an old man. Shortly after he got to Mexico, Sequoyah became very sick and died.

The Cherokee people and the whole country were sad. Everyone knew they had lost a great and wise man.

Today the tallest trees in the world, the giant redwoods, are called sequoias. They are named for the small lame boy who became the greatest Cherokee of them all—the man who brought a great gift to his people—the written word.

Other Places

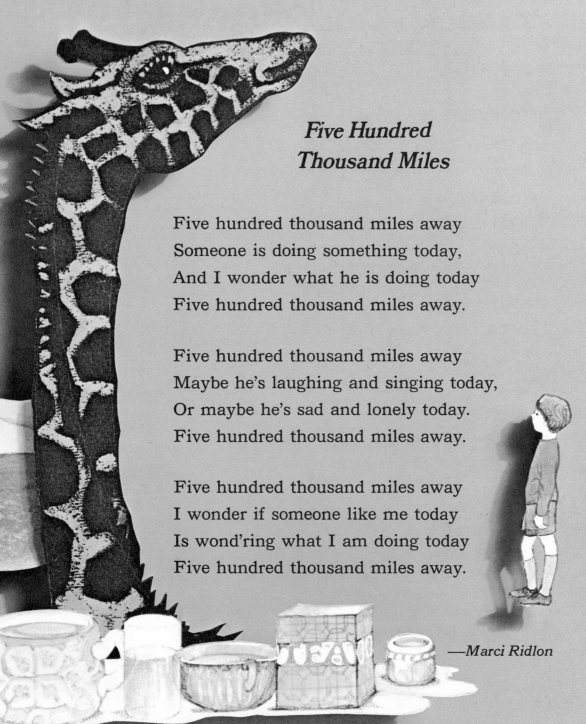

Five Hundred Thousand Miles

Five hundred thousand miles away
Someone is doing something today,
And I wonder what he is doing today
Five hundred thousand miles away.

Five hundred thousand miles away
Maybe he's laughing and singing today,
Or maybe he's sad and lonely today.
Five hundred thousand miles away.

Five hundred thousand miles away
I wonder if someone like me today
Is wond'ring what I am doing today
Five hundred thousand miles away.

—*Marci Ridlon*

Tikki Tikki Tembo

Arlene Mosel

Once upon a time, a long, long time ago, all the fathers and mothers in China used to give their first and honored sons great long names. But second sons were given hardly any name at all.

In a small mountain village there lived a mother who had two little sons. Her second son she called Chang, which means "little or nothing." But her first and honored son, she called **Tikki tikki tembo-no sa rembo-chari bari ruchi-pip peri pembo.** It means "the most wonderful thing in the whole wide world!"

Every morning the mother went to wash in a little stream near her home. The two boys always went along with her. On the bank was an old well.

"Don't go near the well," the mother told them, "or you will surely fall in."

The boys did not always mind their mother. One day they were playing beside the well and on the well when Chang fell in!

Tikki tikki tembo-no sa rembo-chari bari ruchi-pip peri pembo ran to his mother as fast as his little legs could carry him.

"Most Honorable Mother," he gasped, "Chang has fallen into the well!"

"The water roars, Priceless Jewel. I cannot hear you," said the mother.

Then Tikki tikki tembo-no sa rembo-chari bari ruchi-pip peri pembo raised his voice.

"Oh, Most Honorable One," he cried, **"Chang has fallen into the well!"**

"That troublesome boy," answered the mother. "Run and get the Old Man With The Ladder to fish him out."

Then Tikki tikki tembo-no sa rembo-chari bari ruchi-pip peri pembo ran as fast as his little legs could carry him to the Old Man With The Ladder.

"Old Man With The Ladder," he gasped, "Chang has fallen into the well. Will you come and fish him out?"

"So," said the Old Man With The Ladder, "Chang has fallen into the well."

And he ran as fast as his old legs could carry him. Step over step, step over step, he went into the well and picked up little Chang. And step over step, step over step, he brought him out of the well.

He pumped the water out of him and pushed the air into him, and pumped the water out of him and pushed the air into him. And soon Chang was just as good as ever!

Now for the next few months the boys went with their mother to wash, but they did not go near the well. One day, however, they ran to the well to eat their rice cakes.

They ate near the well. They played around the well. They walked on the well. And Tikki tikki tembo-no sa rembo-chari bari ruchi-pip peri pembo fell into the well!

Chang ran as fast as his little legs could carry him to the stream where his mother had gone to wash.

"Oh, Most Honorable Mother," he gasped, "Tikki tikki tembo-no sa rembo-chari bari ruchi-pip peri pembo has fallen into the well!"

"The water roars, Little One. Speak up. I cannot hear you," said the mother.

So little Chang took a deep breath and raised his voice.

"Oh, Mother, Most Honorable," he shouted, **"Tikki tikki tembo-no sa rembo-chari bari ruchi-pip peri pembo has fallen into the well!"**

"Troublesome Child, didn't you hear me tell you to speak up? The water roars. What are you trying to say?" said his mother.

**"Honorable Mother!
Chari bari
rembo
tikki tikki,"**
he gasped,
"pip pip has fallen into the well!"

"My Poor Son, honor your brother. Speak his name carefully," said the mother.

Poor little Chang was all out of breath from saying that great long name, and he didn't think he could say it one more time. But then he thought of his brother in the old well.

Chang bowed his little head clear to the sand and took a deep breath.

Slowly, very slowly, in a raised voice he said, **"Most Honorable Mother, Tikki tikki tembo-no sa rembo-chari bari ruchi-pip peri pembo is at the bottom of the well."**

"Oh, not my first and honored son, my Priceless Jewel! Run quickly and tell the Old Man With The Ladder that your brother has fallen into the well," said the mother.

So Chang ran as fast as his little legs
would carry him to the Old Man With
The Ladder. Under a tree the Old Man
With The Ladder sat bowed and silent.

"**Old Man, Old Man,**" shouted Chang,
"**come right away! Tikki tikki tempo-nosa
rembo-chari bari ruchi-pip peri pembo
has fallen into the stone well!**"

But there was no answer. For a second
Chang waited. Then with his very last
bit of breath he shouted, "**Old Man
With The Ladder, Tikki tikki tembo-no
sa rembo-chari bari ruchi-pip peri pembo
is at the bottom of the well.**"

"Troublesome child, you wake me from
a wonderful dream. I had floated into a
deep blue mist and found myself young
again. There were beautiful flowers
and jewels. If I close my eyes, the dream
may again return."

Poor little Chang was frightened. How could he say that long name again? He bowed clear to the ground.

"Please, Old Man With The Ladder," he cried, "please help my brother out of the cold well."

"So," said the Old Man With The Ladder, "your mother's Priceless Jewel has fallen into the well!"

The Old Man With The Ladder hurried as fast as his old legs could carry him. Step over step, step over step, he went into the well. And step over step, step over step, he went out of the well with the little boy in his arms. Then he pumped the water out of him and pushed the air into him, and pumped the water out of him and pushed the air into him.

But little Tikki tikki tembo-no sa
rembo-chari bari ruchi-pip peri pembo had
been in the water so long, all because of
his great long name, that it was many
weeks before he was quite the same again.

And from that day to this the fathers
and mothers of China have always thought
it wise to give all their children little
short names rather than great long names.

The Optimist

The optimist fell ten stories,
And at each window bar
He shouted to the folks inside:
"Doing all right so far!"

—Anonymous

Gumdrop on the Move

Val Biro

Mr. Oldcastle liked old cars. He had a small brown car, a 1934 Austin. He kept it in a garage with a green door. There was another little garage with a red door. But it had no car in it.

"In there," he said to his grandson Robert, "I had another car once. It was blue with a black top and a shiny horn — a real vintage Austin 1926. I had to sell it years ago."

Just then the mail came. There, with all the letters, was a notice about "The Auction of Vintage Cars." And on the first page was a picture.

Mr. Oldcastle became very excited. *"Look!"* he said. *"Here it is! This is the very car that I had all those years ago. It must be Gumdrop!"*

And it was. When Mr. Oldcastle went to the auction the next day, there, sure enough, was Gumdrop. Many people wanted to buy it.

Mr. Carstairs wanted Gumdrop because he had a collection of vintage cars. Mr. Banger wanted Gumdrop because he sold cars. And Mr. Oldcastle wanted Gumdrop because he once owned it himself.

The auction began. One after another people bid. The one who bid the most got the car.

Many cars were sold this way until it was Gumdrop's turn. "What am I bid for this wonderful car?" shouted the man in charge of the auction.

People bid quickly for Gumdrop, and the price got higher and higher. At last the man cried, "Going, going, gone! Sold to Mr. Banger!"

Mr. Carstairs did not buy it after all because Gumdrop wasn't rare enough for him. "And I couldn't buy it," said Mr. Oldcastle sadly to Robert, "because Gumdrop wasn't cheap enough for me."

Mr. Banger cleaned Gumdrop until it shone and put it with all the new cars in the window of his showroom. "This old car should help to sell my new cars," he said.

Many people stopped to look at Gumdrop, but only a few of them bought new cars. Mr. Banger was disappointed.

Arthur Carson came into the shop one day. "Will you sell me that blue vintage Austin there? I want to race it at Silverstone," he said.

"I might as well," said Mr. Banger, "because after all the car isn't new enough for me."

So Arthur took Gumdrop to his garage. There he removed the top so that Gumdrop could go faster. He took off the shiny horn and put it into the toolbox. Next day he raced Gumdrop at Silverstone.

The vintage cars were tearing around the course. Gumdrop went faster and faster, but the other cars went faster and faster still. Suddenly there was a noise in the engine. Gumdrop stopped.

"That's the front end!" cried Arthur. "I'm out of the race!" He was very disappointed.

Rocky Crasher came to help push Gumdrop off the course. "I'll buy this car from you," he said. "I want to race it at Brightstar."

"You can have it," said Arthur, "because after all the car isn't fast enough for me."

Rocky took Gumdrop to his garage so he could fix the front end. Then he removed the fenders and lamps to make Gumdrop light. And he painted the car yellow with green stripes.

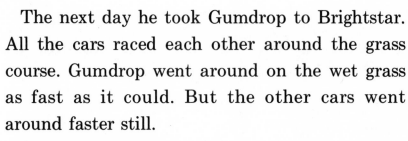

The next day he took Gumdrop to Brightstar. All the cars raced each other around the grass course. Gumdrop went around on the wet grass as fast as it could. But the other cars went around faster still.

Suddenly Gumdrop spun around and stopped. "My wheel has come off!" cried Rocky. "I'm out of the race!" He was very disappointed.

Sandy Boardman came to help with the wheel. "Will you sell me your car?" he asked. "I want to race it at the Bridgetown-hill-climb."

"I will," said Rocky Crasher, "because after all the car isn't light enough for me."

So Sandy Boardman took Gumdrop to his garage. There he removed the running boards and the extra wheel. He then oiled Gumdrop for the big hill-climb.

The next day Sandy and Gumdrop were at Bridgetown. The other cars raced up the hill with roaring engines. Gumdrop went as fast as it could, but the hill was too much for it. Gumdrop's engine was roaring, too, until there was steam coming out of the front end, and Gumdrop had to stop.

"We're out of the race!" cried Sandy. He was very disappointed.

Farmer Small came to help with a can of water. "That's a handy car you've got there," he said. "It would help me on the farm."

"You can have it," said Sandy Boardman, "because after all the car isn't strong enough for me."

So Mr. Small took Gumdrop to his farm. There he removed the number plates. Then he took out the back seat to make room for the corn and the straw that he wanted Gumdrop to carry. Even so, there wasn't enough room. Mr. Small was very disappointed.

"I'll just have to leave it in the yard," he said, "because after all the car isn't big enough for me."

Gumdrop stayed at the farm. Without a top, horn, lamps, fenders, running boards, extra wheel, number plates, back seat, or doors, Gumdrop was a strange and sorry sight.

Gumdrop Finds a Home

One day Mike Manson saw Gumdrop. "That's a funny old car," he thought. "But it might get me a dollar or two at the junkyard."

There was nobody around, so he quickly jumped into Gumdrop and drove it out of the yard.

Mike Manson drove badly and too fast. He bumped into a small brown car that was standing by the roadside. It was Mr. Oldcastle's baby Austin of 1934. Mr. Oldcastle was there himself, trying to fix a flat tire. And he was very angry.

"Look where you're going," he shouted. **"You've put a dent in my car, and you nearly got me!"**

Mike was scared. "I'm sorry," he said. "I can't pay for what I've done to your car. Tell you what. You can have this old car!" Without waiting for an answer, he jumped over the fence and ran away. After all, Gumdrop wasn't worth enough for Mike.

Mr. Oldcastle looked at Gumdrop. "Strange-looking car," he said, "though it is a vintage Austin. And I could restore it. It would be wonderful to have a vintage Austin again." So he tied Gumdrop to his car and drove home.

The next day Mr. Oldcastle and Robert drove to the junkyard to look for the missing parts for Gumdrop. Old cars were piled up everywhere.

"Funny you should ask me," said Alexander Horn, the junkman. "Quite a lot a vintage Austin parts have come in lately. You can have the lot."

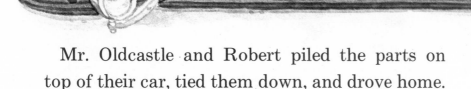

Mr. Oldcastle and Robert piled the parts on top of their car, tied them down, and drove home.

Then they began to restore the car. They put back the fenders, the running boards, the lamps, and the doors. They put on the top and put in the back seat. They put the extra wheel in place. Then they painted the body blue and the fenders black. After a week of hard work, the car looked as good as new.

"It looks exactly like my old car now," said Mr. Oldcastle. "I wish this car were really Gumdrop."

Just then Robert was looking in the toolbox while Mr. Oldcastle cleaned the engine. "I wonder," he thought, "if after all..." He looked at the engine number. C4478. *"The same!"* he shouted. *"The same number! This must really be..."*

"It is! It is!" shouted Robert in turn, as he pulled out the shiny horn. *"This is our own Gumdrop after all!"*

So Mr. Oldcastle got Gumdrop back again. He drove proudly to the town the next week to take part in the Vintage Car Show. Farmer Small was there, and he gave Mr. Oldcastle Gumdrop's number plates which he had taken off. The Mayor was there, and he gave Mr. Oldcastle a silver cup for "The Best Restored Vintage Car."

And there, too, were all the people who had owned Gumdrop since the Vintage Auction. They came up to shake hands with Mr. Oldcastle.

There was Mr. Carstairs, for whom Gumdrop wasn't rare enough. There was Mr. Banger, for whom Gumdrop wasn't new enough.

There was Arthur Carson, for whom Gumdrop wasn't fast enough. There was Rocky Crasher, for whom Gumdrop wasn't light enough.

There was Sandy Boardman, for whom Gumdrop wasn't strong enough. There was Farmer Small, for whom Gumdrop wasn't big enough. There was Mike Manson, for whom Gumdrop wasn't worth enough.

And there was Mr. Oldcastle, who got his old car back. For him Gumdrop was worth more than enough.

The Golden Treasure

Maryke Reesink

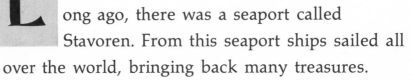

Long ago, there was a seaport called Stavoren. From this seaport ships sailed all over the world, bringing back many treasures.

There was one family in the town that had great wealth. They had only one child, a little girl. She had dolls and toys of all kinds to play with and pretty clothes to wear, but she was never happy and always wanted more.

When she grew up, she owned more ships than anyone else, and she lived in the biggest house in Stavoren. Still, she was not happy. She wasn't very kind and people called her "Proud Lady."

One night a wild storm blew up, bringing ships at sea into the port of Stavoren.

Alone in her big house, with the wind tearing at the windows and the door, sat the Proud Lady. Suddenly, someone knocked loud and long at the door. In came a sea captain.

"Why have you come here on such a night?" asked the lady.

"For years I have sailed the high seas," he answered. "Always I have heard that your ships are the biggest and the best. This storm blew my ship into your port. Now that I am here I would like to sail one of your ships wherever you wish."

Because the lady always sent her ships on long hard trips, most men did not like to work for her. She liked the looks of this sea captain, so she said, "My new ship, *The Golden Treasure*, needs a skipper. He must be a man who will sail the seas, to places where no ship has gone before. And he must bring back to me whatever is most precious in the whole world."

The skipper was silent for a long time. Then he said slowly, "If you will give me *The Golden Treasure*, I will sail her over the seas and the oceans until I have found what is most precious on earth. Then I will bring it back to you."

"Then sail tomorrow!" said the lady.

he next day *The Golden Treasure* set sail.
After many weeks it reached a place known
for its beautiful glass. The people in this town
made great balls of glass so light they seemed to
float in the air like balloons.

The skipper thought how beautiful these glass
balls would be in the lady's house. Still, something
even more precious might be found, so he set sail
again to keep looking.

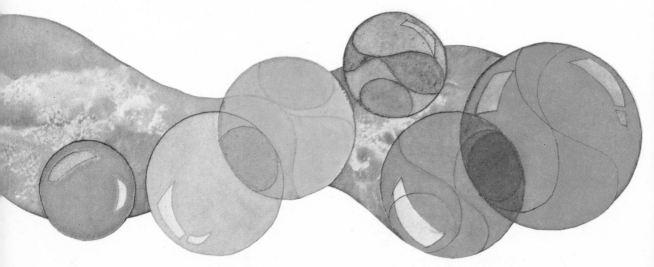

Months and months went by, and at last *The
Golden Treasure* came to a country where all the
people wore silk clothes. Beautiful silks filled the
shops. For children, there were dolls so lifelike
they seemed almost like children themselves.

The captain and his crew couldn't believe their
eyes. Then the captain remembered that the lady
had a beautiful silk dress. And since she had no
children to love the dolls, he did not buy anything.
The Golden Treasure set sail again.

The weather got hotter and hotter. At last, there
was no more water on board for the crew, so *The
Golden Treasure* sailed into a quiet lagoon. A stream
of clear water ran into the lagoon, and coconuts
and fruits of all kinds grew on trees near the shore.
These would be treasures to fill the lady's silver
dishes. But there might be something even more
precious in another place. So *The Golden Treasure*
sailed out of the lagoon.

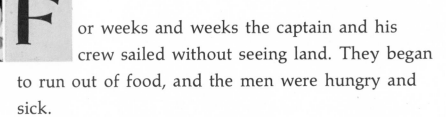

For weeks and weeks the captain and his crew sailed without seeing land. They began to run out of food, and the men were hungry and sick.

At last the lookout called, "Land!" And the next day *The Golden Treasure* sailed up a wide river. On either side lay fields of golden wheat. Where there is wheat, there is bread. The hungry men could eat again!

The skipper let the golden grain run through his fingers. This was the most precious thing in the whole world, for it would give food to hungry people everywhere.

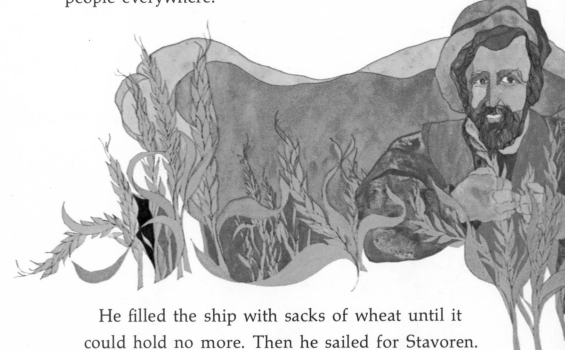

He filled the ship with sacks of wheat until it could hold no more. Then he sailed for Stavoren.

E very day for three years, the lady had gone
to the shore to look for *The Golden Treasure*.
She dreamed of the great wealth it would bring her
and never noticed there were poor and hungry
people in the town. At last one morning,
The Golden Treasure sailed into port.

"What have you brought me?" the lady called to
the captain.

"Gold!" he answered. "Golden wheat—the most
precious thing in the world!"

When the lady saw that there were no furs, no
silk or gold or silver, only ugly sacks of grain,
she was very angry. She turned to the captain
and said, "You call this precious! Throw it
overboard—all of it!"

"It is wheat—bread for the hungry," said the
captain to the proud lady.

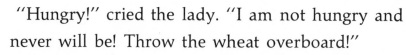

"Hungry!" cried the lady. "I am not hungry and never will be! Throw the wheat overboard!"

Though the townspeople asked her to stop it, one by one the sacks of wheat were thrown overboard and sank to the bottom of the sea. Then the lady turned to the skipper, but he had disappeared.

s time went by, the wheat began to grow. It grew until it reached above the water, but no grain ever grew on the plants.

The growing wheat held sand and mud in place so that the port of Stavoren filled up with it. Ships could no longer sail in.

Most of the townspeople moved to other places. The people who stayed became very poor.

At last, even the Proud Lady had to leave. Many of her ships had been lost at sea. She had sold all her treasures for food. Nothing was left of her great wealth. As poor and hungry as anyone else, she went from village to village looking for bread and a place to sleep.

She thought many times of the sacks of wheat that had been thrown into the sea. Then she had had bread and was not hungry.

One night, she came to a small town. Seeing a man at a door, she started toward him. As she got closer to him, she thought he was someone she had known before. All at once she was sure. It was the captain.

The lady bowed her head and said, "I should have given the wheat to the people who were hungry."

"You know now that there is nothing more precious in all the world," said the captain. Then he took her into his house and gave her a chair by the fire.

But to this day the seaport of Stavoren is filled with mud and sand, and no proud ships sail in or out.

From Port to Port

The word *port* comes from the Latin word *portare* which means *to carry.* It is the root of many words.

porter   report   portable

Which of the three words above means *able to be carried from place to place?*

Which word means *someone who carries things?*

Which word means *to carry back information?*

In what other words do you find *port?*

Barbara K. Walker

The Round Sultan and the Straight Answer

Once there was a sultan who
loved to eat. Three or four times a day
he sat himself down at his table.
One after another, he ate

yogurt soup
and rice with yogurt
and meats with yogurt
and fruits with yogurt.

Great heaps of dark brown bread just
melted away.

Mealtimes were wonderful for the
sultan. Music was played. Birds sang in
their cages.

Each day, the sultan looked in the
mirror. He smiled to see that he was
growing at last to be a fine big sultan.
He must surely be the fattest, roundest
sultan in all the world, he thought.

One day the sultan found that he was too fat to walk a step. His feet hurt if he stood up, even for a minute. His royal throne got a crack, and a new one had to be made.

One by one, the sultan's royal shirts and royal pants tore. He had to have all new clothes, much larger than his old ones.

The sultan could no longer fit into the royal bathtub. A new one was made, large enough to hold two elephants. Ten men helped the sultan into the bathtub. Ten men helped the sultan out again.

Clearly, the sultan had become too fat. Something had to be done.

A crier went out all over the kingdom.

> HEAR YE!   HEAR YE!
> The Sultan has become too fat. He must have a doctor to help him become thin again. Who can help the Sultan? Your prize will be great.

Doctors hurried to the castle from all parts of the kingdom. Each one was sure he could help the sultan.

The first doctor looked at the sultan. Then he said, "My Sultan, you must eat nothing but fruit."

The sultan tried for a week to eat nothing but fruit. He had fruit for breakfast, lunch, afternoon tea, and dinner. He tried to eat nothing but fruit. Oh, he ate between meals now and then. A pile of rice with meat made a fine snack. And nothing was better than a few plates of honey cakes.

At the end of a week, the first doctor came to see the sultan. The sultan was fatter than ever.

"To the dungeon with him!" shouted the sultan. **"Give him nothing but fruit As for me, fruit just won't do."**

A second doctor looked at the sultan. Then he said, "My Sultan, you must take nothing but hot tea."

The sultan tried for a week to take nothing but hot tea. He had hot tea for breakfast, hot tea for lunch, hot tea for afternoon tea, and then hot tea for dinner. Oh, he ate between meals now and then, because he was so hungry. A pile of rice with meat made a fine snack. And he did love honey cakes.

At the end of the week, the second doctor came to see the sultan. The sultan was fatter than ever.

"To the dungeon with him!" shouted the sultan. **"Give him nothing but hot tea. As for me, hot tea just won't do."**

More doctors came. "Give the sultan steam baths every day," said one.

The sultan had one steam bath after another for a week. Between baths he ate and ate. Off to the dungeon went another doctor.

"Nothing but meat!"
said one doctor.
"Smaller helpings!"
said the next doctor.
"No music at meals!"
said another.
"Less sleep!"
"Nothing but yogurt!"
"Give him these special pills!"

One after another, forty doctors tried to help the sultan. One after another, forty doctors went off to the dungeon.

As for the sultan, he grew even fatter.

The Forty Days

One day a wise hamal passed the castle. On his back he carried the furniture of a whole house.

"Hamal!" called the sultan's page. "You are needed in the castle."

The hamal set down the furniture. He hurried after the page until he came before the sultan.

"You can carry the furniture from a whole house," said the page. "Lift our sultan into his bed."

For a minute the hamal looked at the sultan. He had heard about the sultan's troubles.

"What does it matter if he sits on his throne or gets into his bed? He will be dead in another forty days anyway!" the hamal said.

The sultan gasped. **"How dare you!"** Then in a soft voice he asked,

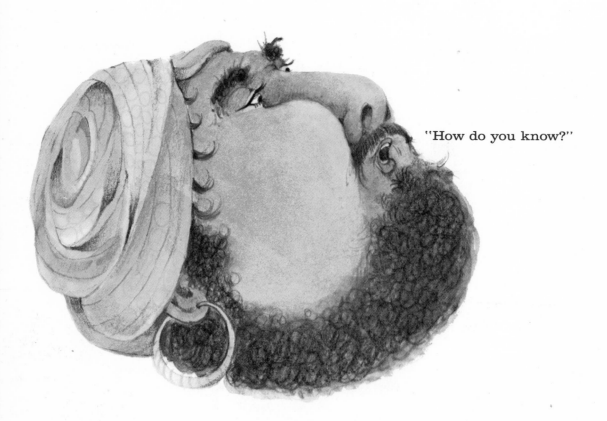

"How do you know?"

"I just **know,**" answered the hamal. "Believe me. You will be dead in forty days."

"He is lying! To the dungeon!" shouted the sultan.

Two men grabbed the hamal and pushed him down the dungeon steps.

As for the sultan, suddenly he was not hungry at all. At breakfast he ate a little brown bread. At lunch he had fruit. At afternoon tea he had a little honey cake. At dinner he ate a small piece of meat. As for eating between meals, somehow food didn't look good to him.

Day after day passed. The sultan sat and worried. At the end of twenty days he got up. His feet felt funny, but he could walk again. He walked the floor hour after hour. Only twenty more days!

His royal shirts and his royal pants began to hang funny. Something strange had happened to them. They were much too big.

At the end of thirty-nine days, the sultan made out his last will. He passed the kingdom on to his younger brother. Who would have thought that the fattest sultan in the world would have ended in such a way?

The last of the forty days came and went. All day the sultan walked the floor. He looked out at the houses below. How sad to leave such a fine kingdom!

The forty-first day came. It was sunny and bright. Birds sang in the trees of the sultan's garden. Suddenly the sultan sat up. This was the forty-first day! He was not dead!

"Send for that hamal!" he cried.

The page hurried down the stone steps to the dungeon. Forty doctors, all of them thin, bowed as he came in.

"This is the forty-first day," said the hamal.

"You are right," said the page. "And the sultan has sent for you."

The hamal followed the page up the steps.

"There you are!" cried the sultan, sitting up in bed. "You said I was to die in forty days. This is the forty-first day. You were lying!"

"That may be," answered the hamal. Then his eyes shone. "But see, My Sultan, **you are thin!**"

For a minute the sultan could not say a word. Then a great smile came over his face. He leaped out of bed. He danced about the room in his royal pajamas. He felt his thin arms, his thin legs, his thin neck. Yes, he was thin.

"Bring me some new scales!" he shouted.

The biggest scales in the kingdom were brought to the sultan. The sultan sat down in the dish at one side of the large scales.

"Now fill up the other dish with gold until the scales are even," ordered the sultan.

The other dish was filled with gold until the great pile was even with the smiling sultan.

"This gold, hamal, is your prize," said the sultan. "Take it, and may your way be open."

The hamal took his treasure with a thankful heart and left the castle.

One by one, the forty doctors climbed the stone steps and went about their work.

As for the sultan, he became no fatter than a sultan should be. And as far as I know, he is a sultan to this day.

After the Party

Jonathan Blake
Ate too much cake,
He isn't himself today;
He's tucked up in bed
With a feverish head,
And he doesn't much care to play.

I'm sorry to state
That he also ate
Six pickles, a pie, and a pear;
In fact I confess
It's a reasonable guess
He ate practically everything there.

Yes, Jonathan Blake
Ate too much cake,
So he's not at his best today;
But there's no need for sorrow—
If you come back tomorrow,
I'm sure he'll be out to play.

—William Wise

When the Drum Sang

Anne Rockwell

One day a little girl named Tselane went down to the river to get water. Dip after dip she worked to fill her large calabash. As she worked, she sang. The song was so beautiful that all the animals around her stopped whatever they were doing and listened.

In the tall grass, not far from Tselane, a man with a drum sat and listened, too. Now if he had been a good man, he would have listened quietly and gone away. But he was not a good man. He was a very bad *zimwe*, and so a bad idea came into his head.

Just as Tselane had almost filled her calabash with water, the man sneaked up behind her and pushed her into his drum.

Before she could cry out, the man said to her, "Little girl, you sing well. Now, listen to me. When I beat this drum, you must sing, as well and as long as you can. If you do not sing, I will beat you instead of my drum!"

Tselane was frightened, and so she told him she would do what he said. The man took his big drum with the little girl inside and went away.

When he came to a village some miles away, it was almost evening. He stopped and asked the chief if he might spend the night. The chief answered that he could. So the man said that he wished to play the drum for all the people to thank them.

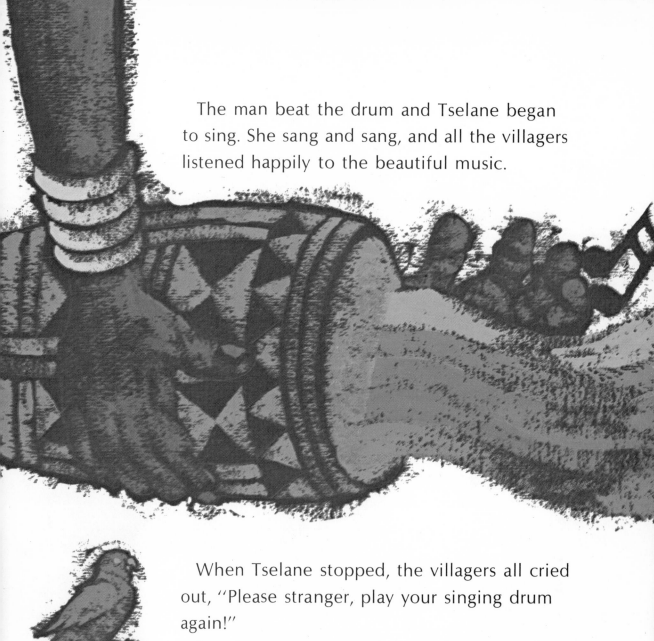

The man beat the drum and Tselane began
to sing. She sang and sang, and all the villagers
listened happily to the beautiful music.

When Tselane stopped, the villagers all cried
out, "Please stranger, play your singing drum
again!"

But the man answered, "I am hungry and
tired, and I cannot play my drum until I eat."

When the people heard this, they hurried to
their gardens and filled their baskets with all
the good things they could find to eat.

After the man had eaten all he could, he beat the drum and Tselane began to sing. She sang until the villagers got tired and went to sleep.

When everyone had gone to bed, the man opened the top of the drum and gave the little girl five small cold beans — all that was left of his big dinner.

When morning came, the man went on to another village, taking his wonderful drum.

Meanwhile, Tselane's parents became worried when their daughter did not return from the river. They went to the river to look for her. All they saw was her calabash filled with water.

A giraffe was eating leaves from the top of a tree and Tselane's parents called to him, "Oh Giraffe, you with your long neck that can see far away, have you seen our little girl?"

But the giraffe shook his head and went on eating.

For weeks and weeks Tselane's parents went from village to village asking for their little girl. But she was not to be found.

One evening, tired and hungry, they stopped at a village and asked to spend the night. The villagers told them that there was another stranger staying in the village that night, but there was still room for more. The other stranger was the man with the singing drum.

The man beat the drum and it began to sing. Inside the drum, Tselane sang songs about the beautiful things she had known when she lived outside the drum. She sang about deer running through tall grass, about the gentle sounds of baby kids, and about tall blue mountains reaching for the sky. Because she was sure she would never see these things again, Tselane sang sad songs about happy things.

When Tselane began to sing, her mother started to cry out, for she knew it was her daughter's voice. But Tselane's father looked crossly at his wife, and so she said nothing. Instead she sat very still and listened.

When the singing was done, the man asked for food and water. While the man ate and drank, Tselane's father sat near him and told him what a wonderful drum he had.

When the man had enough to eat, he fell asleep. Tselane's parents waited until all the villagers were asleep. Then they went quietly over to the drum, untied the top covering, and looked inside. There was their little girl, thin and frightened and lonely.

"Come out, come out," they said quietly and held her tight.

Then Tselane's father took a little fire on a stick and went into the forest.

He held the stick of fire near a hole in an old tree. After a few minutes many bees came out of the hole. They did not like the smoke from the man's fire.

Tselane's father put the stick close to the bees, and they flew ahead of him to get away from the smoke. In this way he drove them back to the village and up to the man's drum. The bees flew into the drum. Tselane's father closed the drum and smiled. Then the family went to sleep.

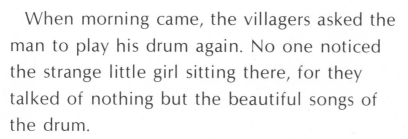

When morning came, the villagers asked the man to play his drum again. No one noticed the strange little girl sitting there, for they talked of nothing but the beautiful songs of the drum.

"I could play the drum quite well, if I only had a little breakfast," said the man.

The people promised him that they would feed him if he would only play one short song before they went into their gardens.

The man began to beat the drum, but nothing happened. He beat the drum again. And nothing happened. A few people began to laugh at him.

Again and again he beat the drum, but nothing happened. By now all the people were laughing at him. Then he threw his drum on the ground. He kicked it and shouted at it, but the drum was silent.

At last he picked up the drum and ran out of the village, shouting to the drum, "I told you I would beat you if you did not sing, and now I will!"

So saying, the man tore off the top of the drum to beat Tselane. But instead of finding Tselane, he found the bees. They flew after him as he ran, and no one ever saw or heard of him again.

As for Tselane, she sang a beautiful, happy song for the people before they went back to their gardens to work. Everyone gave her good things to eat and a pretty necklace besides. Then Tselane and her parents began their long trip home.

Same Sound - Different Words

Some words sound just the same but are spelled differently and have different meanings. Look at the underlined words in each pair of sentences. Match the sentences with the pictures.

You are pretty, <u>dear.</u>
You are pretty, <u>deer.</u>

Did you see that <u>sail?</u>
Did you see that <u>sale?</u>

Use these words in sentences.

| piece | hole | meat |
| peace | whole | meet |

How Encyclopedia Brown Solved the Case of the Silver Fruit Bowl...

Chief Brown's words showed Encyclopedia where Mr. Herman had been lying.

Chief Brown said that the silver fruit bowl was rounded inside like a big spoon. Mr. Herman could not have had a good idea of what the holdup man looked like by looking into the fruit bowl, as he had said.

Look into a shiny spoon. What do you see? You see yourself as in a mirror, but **upside down!**

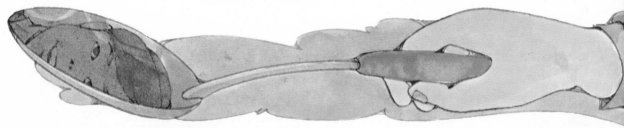

Faced with these facts, Mr. Herman told the real story. He had made up the story of the holdup man. He had stolen the silver dishes himself, hoping to sell them in another city and to keep all the money.

Glossary

This glossary gives the pronunciations and meanings of some of the words used in this book.

The pronunciation is shown just after the word in this way: able (ā′ bl). The letters and signs are pronounced as shown in the words listed below.

If the word has more than one syllable, as in the example, a heavy accent mark ′ is placed after the syllable that receives the heaviest stress.

PRONUNCIATION KEY

a	hat	i	it	p	paper	v	very
ā	face	ī	ice	r	run	w	will
ã	care	j	jam	s	say	y	yes
ä	father	k	kind	sh	she	z	zoo
b	bad	l	land	t	tell	zh	treasure
ch	child	m	me	th	thin		
d	did	n	no	ŦH	then		
e	let	ng	long	u	cut	ə	stands for
ē	be	o	hot	ủ	pull		a in about
ėr	her	ō	open	ü	June		e in given
f	fat	ô	or	ū	use		i in family
g	go	oi	oil				o in button
h	he	ou	out				u in walrus

THE PRONUNCIATION SYSTEM AND KEY ARE ADAPTED FROM *THORNDIKE-BARNHART JUNIOR DICTIONARY* BY E. L. THORNDIKE AND CLARENCE L. BARNHART, COPYRIGHT © 1968 BY SCOTT, FORESMAN AND COMPANY.

A

able (ā′ bl) having the power needed to do something

afford (ə fôrd′) to be able to pay for without hardship: *We can afford a new rug.*

alligator (al′ ə gā′ tər) a large lizard with a long body, short legs, strong jaws

aluminum (ə lü′ mə nəm) **1.** a metal that is strong but light in weight. **2.** made of aluminum: *Mother bought aluminum pots.*

America (ə mer′ ə kə) **1.** The United States. **2.** North America and South America.

American (ə mer′ ə kən) **1.** coming from or belonging to America: *Apple pie is an American dish.* **2.** Someone born or living in the United States

annual (an′ yù əl) coming once a year

art (ärt) **1.** the way or method of doing something. **2.** works, such as paintings, made by practicing an art

ashamed (ə shāmd′) feeling uneasy, sorry, or to blame

aside (ə sīd′) away or set off to the side

attic (at′ ik) the part of a building just below the roof, sometimes used as a place to store things

auction (ôk′ shən) a sale in which things are sold to the one who offers or bids the most money

B

band (band) people who play music together

bargain (bär′ gən) **1.** to be able to make a deal on price: *We had to bargain about the price.* **2.** a good buy

baton (ba ton′) a stick or rod used by the director of a music group for beating time and leading the group

beating (bēt′ ing) **1.** a spanking. **2.** hitting over and over again. **3.** having the sound made by beating: *We heard the beating drums.*

bill (bil) **1.** a piece of paper money. **2.** a bird's mouth

billboard (bil′ bôrd′) a board carrying a sign or an ad

billfold (bil′ fōld) a folding purse for bills or paper money

block (blok) a four-cornered space in a town or city with a street on each side

board (bôrd) **1.** a piece of wood. **2.** a flat frame made for a special purpose: *Amy saw the sign on the bulletin board.* **3.** to be on a ship, plane, or train: *There were twenty people on board the ship.*

bow (bou) to bend from the waist

---

hat, fāce, cāre, fäther, let, bē, hėr, it, īce, hot, ōpen, ôr, oil, out, cut, pùll, Jüne, ūse, thin, ₮Hen; ə stands for a in about, e in given, i in family, o in button, u in walrus.

bow (bō) **1.** a tie made of ribbon or piece of cloth. **2.** something used for shooting arrows. **3.** a rod strung with horse hair and used in playing the violin. See **violin.**

brain (brān) **1.** the mind or intelligence. **2.** someone who solves a mystery or is very bright: *Herman was the brain behind the plan.*

bridge (brij) **1.** something that carries a road over a body of water or land. **2.** the part of a violin that holds the strings up. See **violin.**

brindle cat (brin′dəl kat) a cat that is gray or tan with darker stripes

bulletin (bùl′ ət n) **1.** a piece of news. **2.** having or carrying news: *The practice times are on the bulletin board.*

C

calabash (kal′ ə bash) a bowl, bottle, or other dish made from the dried shell of some fruit

calico (kal′ ə kō) a cheap cotton cloth, often having bright patterns

California (kal′ ə fôrn′ yə) one of the fifty states of the United States, located in the Far West on the Pacific Ocean

careful (kãr′ fəl) watchful; taking care; giving thought to

carelessly (kãr′ lis lē) without any thought

case (kās) **1.** a matter for the law. **2.** a box or covering

Cherokee (cher′ ə kē) **1.** the name of a tribe of North American Indians that once lived in Tennessee and North Carolina. **2.** a member of the Cherokee tribe. **3.** the language of the Cherokee people

chief (chēf) **1.** the head or leader; **2.** main; most important

china (chī′ nə) fine dishes made first in the country of China

china-blue (chī′ nə blü) gray-blue; the shade of blue used in the pattern of some china

chores (chôrz) everyday jobs: *On a farm milking cows and feeding the animals are everyday chores.*

clarinet (klar ə net′) a wind instrument with a reed played by blowing through a mouthpiece and pressing keys

claws (klôz) sharp, hooked nails on the feet of some animals such as birds and cats

clerk (klėrk) someone who sells things in a store

comics (kom′ iks) strips of pictures with words and balloons that tell stories

control (kən trōl′) **1.** the power over

something or someone. **2.** to bring someone or something into line

cornmeal (kôrn' mēl) corn ground into a powder used in making bread or cakes

crew (krü) the men who do the work on a ship or plane

crib (krib) a small bed with high sides; a baby's bed

crowd (kroud) a large gathering

crutches (kruch' əz) two supports made of wood or aluminum and used by lame people to help them walk

D

dangerous (dān' jər əs) not safe; having the power to hurt or harm

dens (denz) **1.** homes of wild animals, many times caves. **2.** hideaways

dent (dent) a hollow caused by a blow

detective (di tek' tiv) someone who solves mysteries

dictionary (dik' shən er' ē) a book that tells what words mean and how to say them

director (də rek' tər) someone who runs a business or tells people how to do things

disappearing (dis' ə pir' ing) **1.** going away or out of sight **2.** being used up

disappointed (dis' ə point' id) unhappy because something did not turn out as hoped for

downbeat (doun' bēt) downswing of the hand or baton by the music director to show the players or singers the first beat of a piece of music

drill (dril) to practice something over and over again

ducked (dukt) made a quick move to keep from being hit, seen, or caught: *The girl ducked behind the tree.*

dungeon (dun' jən) a dark jail, usually underground

E

encyclopedia (en sī' klə pē' dē ə) a book or set of books filled with facts in alphabetical order

engine (en' jən) a machine that can make something move

England (ing' lənd) an island country off the western shores of Europe

English (ing' lish) **1.** people born or living in England. **2.** belonging to or coming from England. **3.** the language of England

exactly (eg zakt' lē) in just the right way

F

fair (fãr) honest; just

---

hat, fāce, cãre, fäther, let, bē, hėr, it, īce, hot, ōpen, ôr, oil, out, cut, pu̇ll, Jüne, ūse, thin, ŦHen; ə stands for a in about, e in given, i in family, o in button, u in walrus.

firecrackers (fīr′krak′ərz) small paper rolls of gunpowder that make a loud bang when lit

flax (flaks) a plant from which thread for linen cloth is made

flour (flour) fine powder made of ground-up wheat and used in making bread and cake

forge (fôrj) a place where metal is melted and hammered into shapes

frame (frām) a case that holds a picture or windowpane

fund (fund) money set aside for special use

G

garlic (gär′ lik) a plant of the onion family, used to flavor foods

general (jen′ ər əl) a leader of an army

gentleman (jen′ təl mən) a man who is polite, kind, honest, and honorable

grating (grāt′ing) crossed bars covering openings in sidewalks or streets

guest (gest) a visitor

H

hamal (hə mäl′) in some countries the name for someone whose job is to carry heavy things

handball (hand′ bôl′) a game in which the hand is used to bat a ball against a wall

hind (hīnd) at the back

holdup (hōld′ up) a theft in which someone is made to hand over goods or money

honor (on′ ər) to think well of

honorable (on′ ər ə bl) worthy of being well thought of

hour (our) sixty minutes

hunger (hung′ gər) the need for food

hut (hut) a small, poorly built house; cabin; shack

I

icicles (ī′ si kəlz) pointed sticks of ice that hang down from a roof, window, or tree

instrument (in′ strə mənt) something that music may be played on

invisible (in viz′ ə bl) out of sight

iron (ī′ ərn) a strong metal used in making pots and building materials; the metal from which steel is made

J

jealous (jel′ əs) wanting something someone else has

jewel (jü′ l) a gem or stone worth much money

June (jün) one of the summer months; the sixth month

K

kingdom (king′ dəm) a land ruled by a king

L

lagoon (lə gün′) a pond joined to a much larger body of water

lame (lām) unable to walk well because of a hurt or weak leg

language (lang′ gwij) written and spoken speech

latch (lach) a catch or something to hold a door or gate closed

law (lô) a rule made by a country, state, or city

less (les) not so much as; a smaller amount: *The bag weighed less than two pounds.*

likely (līk′ lē) almost a sure thing: *Because of the storm, Allen is likely to be late.*

limp (limp) not stiff; very weak

M

magnet (mag′ nit) a piece of iron or steel that can draw to it other things made of iron or steel

manage (man′ ij) to run; to control; to lead

manager (man′ ij ər) someone who runs things; boss; director

medal (med′ l) a pin or ribbon given to honor a brave or good deed

Mexicali (mek′ sə kal ē) from a city in Mexico just south of California

Mexican (mek′ sə kən) **1.** belonging to or coming from Mexico. **2.** one who was born or who lives in Mexico

Mexico (mek′ sə kō) the country that lies to the south of the United States

mist (mist) a light fog; cloud of damp air

mistake (mis tāk′) a wrong or unwise answer or act

mount (mount) a high hill or mountain

Mount Vernon (mount vėr′ nən) the home of George Washington

N

neighborhood (na′ bər hůd) **1.** a place where people live or work near one another. **2.** the people living or working in a place

O

orchestra (ôr′ kis trə) a group of people who play music on different instruments, including violins and string instruments as well as horns and other band instruments

---

hat, fāce, cãre, fäther, let, bē, hėr, it, īce, hot, ōpen, ôr, oil, out, cut, půll, Jüne, ūse, thin, ŦHen; ə stands for a in about, e in given, i in family, o in button, u in walrus.

order (ôr′ dər) **1.** a state of quiet, peace, or harmony. **2.** with *in*, to bring about: *We have to cross a bridge in order to get to the town.* **3.** the way things are arranged

P

pail (pāl) something used to carry water; a bucket

painting (pān′ ting) a picture made by using paints or colors

parade (pə rād′) **1.** a march with or without music to show off a group of people, animals, or things. **2.** having to do with a parade: *First came the parade horses.*

pattern (pat′ ərn) the way lines and colors are arranged

pegs (pegz) **1.** wooden nails. **2.** parts of a stringed instrument, used to tighten or loosen the strings. See **violin.**

peppers (pep′ ərz) red or green vegetables that may be used in soup or some other dish

pest (pest) someone who keeps bothering others or causing trouble

pester (pes′ tər) to bother someone; to keep after

pitch (pich) a black, thick material taken from tar and used to cover roads

plucked (pluckt) picked or pulled at; played a stringed instrument that way: *Sandy plucked the strings of the violin.*

poor (pür) **1.** having few things or little money; lacking something. **2.** needing comfort or pity

president (prez′ ə dənt) the chief leader of a group, such as the people of a country

prickled (prik′ əld) tingled

project (proj′ ekt) an undertaking; a plan

pump (pump) **1.** something that may be used to lift or move air or water up into or out of something. **2.** to move air or water by means of a pump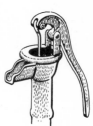

R

rack (rak) a frame with hangers for holding things

remind (ri mīnd′) to make someone remember or think of

restore (ri stôr′) to return; to put back or rebuild

return (ri tėrn′) to go back, put back, or give back

row (rō) a line: *Stanley weeded the row of beans.*

royal (roi′ l) belonging to a king or queen

S

saddle (sad′ l) a seat for a rider on horseback

sags (sagz) dips, sinks, or bends because of weight

scales (skālz) an instrument for weighing things or people

scalp (skalp) the skin on the top and back of the head

science (sī′ əns) **1.** the body of facts and laws that explain events; knowledge. **2.** a branch of learning, such as biology

scout (skout) **1.** someone sent ahead to find things out or explore. **2.** a member of the Boy Scouts or Girl Scouts. **3.** having to do with or belonging to a scout

second (sek′ ənd) **1.** coming after the first. **2.** one of the sixty small parts of time that make up a minute. **3.** a short span of time

sequoias (si kwoi′ əz) giant redwood trees of California

Sequoyah (si kwoi′ ə) the great Indian leader who invented or made up a

way of writing the Cherokee language and for whom the redwoods, or Sequoias, are named

shaggy (shag′ ē) covered with or made of long thick hair; very hairy

sill (sil) the piece of wood at the bottom of a window or door

skipper (skip′ ər) a captain of a ship

snatched (snatcht) took quickly; grabbed

sneakers (snēk′ ərz) shoes made of heavy cloth with rubber soles, worn for play

snout (snout) a long nose, especially of an animal such as a pig

snuggling (snug′ ling) curling up beside; moving close to

solid (sol′ id) hard; firm; strong

spinning wheel (spin′ing hwēl) something for spinning flax or cotton into thread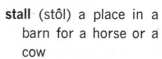

stall (stôl) a place in a barn for a horse or a cow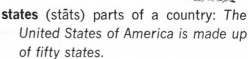

states (stāts) parts of a country: *The United States of America is made up of fifty states.*

station (stā′ shən) **1.** headquarters for policemen or firemen. **2.** a stopping place

---

hat, fāce, cāre, fäther, let, bē, hėr, it, īce, hot, ōpen, ôr, oil, out, cut, pủll, Jūne, ūse, thin, ŦHen; ə stands for a in about, e in given, i in family, o in button, u in walrus.

steam (stēm) **1.** the gas made by boiling water. **2.** having steam. **3.** to use steam

steel (stēl) **1.** a strong product made from iron. **2.** made of steel

stickball (stik′ bôl′) a game like baseball, played with a stick instead of a bat

strange (strānj) **1.** not known. **2.** not understood. **3.** odd or queer

stuffing (stuf′ ing) filling

stump (stump) the part of the tree that is left after most of it has been cut off

sultan (sult′ n) in some countries, the ruler or king

supper (sup′ ər) a light evening meal when dinner is eaten at noon

syllabary (sil′ ə ber′ ē) a system of writing in which each letter stands for a syllable

syllable (sil′ ə bl) a word or part of a word spoken as a unit and made up of at least one vowel sound: *The word* spin *has one syllable. The word* spinning *has two syllables.*

T

tailor (tā′ lər) someone whose job is to make clothes

tape (tāp) a thin strip of cloth, paper, or plastic with a sticky side used in wrapping packages and in making labels or name tags

teatime (tē′ tīm′) a time for rest and something to eat and drink, usually in late afternoon

telescope (tel′ ə skōp) an instrument that makes faraway things such as stars seem closer and bigger

thoughtful (thôt′ fəl) **1.** full of thought; deep in thought. **2.** having the look of being deep in thought

tom-tom (tom′ tom′) a drum, usually beaten by the hands: *The Indians played the tom-tom at their dances.*

trade (trād) **1.** the act of giving and getting things. **2.** to give something in exchange for something else.

treasure (trezh′ ər) something of great worth

trembling (trem′ bling) shaking because of a strong feeling such as fear or from the cold

tribe (trīb) a group of people with the same customs, language, and leader

trombone (trom′ bōn) a horn that has a long sliding piece that is moved to make different sounds

trot (trot) the way a horse moves when it lifts its right front foot and back left foot at the same time; something between a walk and a run

true (trü) that which is so; not false

trumpet (trum′ pit) a horn that is played by blowing into a mouthpiece and pressing keys to make different sounds

trundle bed (trun′ dəl bed) a low bed that may be stored under a bigger bed

U

United States (ū nīt′ id stāts) country made up of fifty states

unlike (un līk′) not like; different from

use (ūz) **1.** to put to work: *Dad said we could use his boat.* **2.** to take or put in: *We use chicken to make this soup.*

use (ūs) being put to work or being used: *Jill made good use of the cookbook.*

V

valley (val′ ē) a broad lowland between hills or mountains

Valley Forge (val′ ē fôrj) a place in Pennsylvania where George Washington and his army spent the winter of 1778

vintage (vin′ tij) having worth because of age

violin (vī′ ə lin′) an instrument with four strings and played with a bow

W

walrus (wôl′ rəs) a sea animal that looks like a seal except for its long tusks

wealth (welth) riches

weight (wāt) heaviness

west (west) **1.** the direction in which the sun sets. **2.** the part of a country that lies toward the west

whole (hōl) all of something

wits (wits) one's mind; ability to think

worth (wėrth) usefulness; importance; value

Y

yogurt (yō′ gėrt) a milk food

Z

Zimwe (zim′ wē) in tales from South Africa, a magic spirit that may appear as a giant, animal, or man, but who is always greedy

---

hat, fāce, cãre, fäther, let, bē, hėr, it, īce, hot, ōpen, ôr, oil, out, cut, pu̇ll, Jüne, ūse, thin, ₮Hen; ə stands for a in about, e in given, i in family, o in button, u in walrus.